Science vs.
A Scientist Highlights Fundamental Flaws in Atheistic Evolution
Evolution

Jeff Miller, Ph.D.

Table of Contents

CHAPTER 8

Genetics vs. Evolution 101

CONCLUSION

APPENDICES

Background

I grew up in a Christian home. My parents taught me to believe in God and the Bible as His inspired Word. As I grew older and could understand more, I asked more questions. So they showed me the evidence that supported those conclusions and taught me the importance of reasoning from the evidence and doing everything—especially studying—to the best of my ability. The church taught me to test or prove a person's statements before believing them—no matter how respected the author of those statements might be (1 Thessalonians 5:21).

I entered my junior high, high school, and college years with the analytical mind I was taught to have, thirsting for knowledge. I was in for a rude awakening. I was informed by school teachers, textbooks, and friends that the biblical account of Creation was wrong. It allegedly did not fit the evidence. Supposedly, there was another option that could explain the origin of the Universe in a naturalistic way—God was not needed in the equation. This option was said to be very scientific—supported by observation and evidence—and yet, in direct opposition to the biblical account. Evolution was the name given to this option.

Naturally, I wanted answers. And I wanted them fast. I knew that both evolution and Creation could not be true, though some might try to mix the two. I had been taught to seek the truth with an open mind, and search for it diligently. I was taught not to fear what I found, because the truth—no matter how hard it is to stomach—is to be prized above all. It will set us free (John 8:32; Proverbs 23:23), I was told, and my experience verified that to be true. But I also knew that the answer to the question, "Is evolution true?" has far reaching implications. The answer would affect my behavior, what I taught others, how I viewed life, how I would rear my children, and could even affect my eternal destiny.

So I began a career as a scientist. I dug in and examined the evidence from many areas of science. My field choice of biomechanical engineering and my specific areas of research allowed me a wider array of scientific study than many scientific disciplines. For years I studied the scientific evidence from a variety of scientific disciplines. I engaged in heavy study in physical science (physics, geology, astronomy, and chemistry) and thermal science (thermodynamics, fluid science, and heat transfer), as well as mechanical science (statics, dynamics, and kinematics), biology, material science, and even acoustics, magnetism, and electrical fields. I studied the scientific evidence for and against the Creation model and the evolutionary model. What have I found? Does the evidence support naturalistic evolution as I was told? This book is dedicated to answering that question.

Scope

There are two conceivable possibilities for how the Universe came into existence. It created itself, or it was created.

1) Either it came about wholly naturally, without supernatural assistance (atheistic evolution).

2) Or it came about with some sort of supernatural assistance.

    a. Many believe that the God of the Bible is the Creator. If so, there are two options for the origin of the Universe:

        i. The Universe came about primarily naturally, with supernatural assistance from God along the way (theistic evolution).

        ii. Or it came about primarily supernaturally by God (Creation).

    b. Others believe that another god(s) exists and is the creator. If so,

        i. The Universe came about primarily naturally, with supernatural assistance from that god(s) along the way (theistic evolution).

ii. Or it came about primarily supernaturally by that god(s) (Creation).

Variations exist for how the Universe could have originated wholly naturally, though the consensus among naturalists is that the Universe came about through some form of spontaneous self-creation and subsequent Big Bang coupled with Darwinian evolution.

Though a presentation of the evidence for the following two propositions is not within the scope of this book (see www.apologeticspress.org), it is important to understand that I am writing with them in mind.

1) It is my belief that the vast majority of the religions of the world, with their alleged "inspired" materials, do not hold up to scrutiny, but rather prove themselves to be of human origin. Only Christianity and its Bible have been able to withstand skeptics' attacks, and stand firm today, set apart from all other religions and religious documents. Based on the evidence, if any religious document can be said to be from the Creator, it would be the Bible, which contains characteristics which cannot be explained through human authors. I believe these propositions can be reasonably proven, and much has been written illustrating these fundamental truths (see www.apologeticspress.org). This eliminates 2)b. and its subpoints from discussion in this book.

2) It is also my firm belief that theistic evolution (i.e., the idea that God exists and evolution is also true) is not compatible with the Bible (see Thompson, 2000). The Creation model is the teaching of the Bible. So if God exists, Jehovah of the Bible is God (based on proposition one). If Jehovah exists, the Bible is His Word, and Creation—not evolution—is true. Furthermore, if Darwinian evolution is found to be inconsistent with the evidence, theistic evolution simultaneously is proven false in light of the evidence. This eliminates 2)a.i. from discussion in this book as well.

On that basis, if the Big Bang Theory and Darwinian evolution are true, atheism is true and the Bible is flawed and uninspired, and its God does not exist. If, on the other hand, it can be shown that naturalistic evolutionary theories cannot provide an adequate explanation for the origin of the Universe that is in keeping with the evidence, then God must exist, that God is the God of the Bible, and Creation is true. Evolution stands with atheism—the two standing or falling together. The same can be said of Creation and theism. With this thesis in mind, this book investigates atheistic evolution to see how it fares when subjected to critical scientific examination. [NOTE: Creationists believe in natural selection and "evolution," as long as evolution is understood to mean small changes within kinds and within very limited parameters, as the evidence indicates. This belief is known as "microevolution," and is supported by the evidence. The naturalist, however, contends that "macroevolution" is also true—that changes can occur which traverse the barriers between kinds of living creatures and that all present species evolved from a single-celled organism through evolution. Macroevolution, which naturalists misleadingly use synonymously with the term evolution (as though they are one and the same), is one of the primary doctrines that is addressed in this book, and, along with cosmic evolution, is what I will be generally referring to when I use the term "evolution."]

Structure

The first portion of this book (through the Conclusion) examines several fundamental scientific principles in light of evolutionary theory. These chapters have been grouped together to allow an uninterrupted flow of the basic argumentation against atheistic evolution. While reading through those chapters, the apologist and the skeptic will perhaps be struck by the fact that many of the most recent and/or typical retorts by evolutionists are not addressed. I have chosen to confine a discussion of those quibbles to appendices in the second half of the book so that they do not distract the reader from the main thrust of each chapter. By making this separation, I do not wish to convey the idea that those appendices are less important than the rest of the book. On the contrary, the majority of the material in the book resides in the appendices.

For the non-Christian or skeptically-minded individual: Naturally, you may have questions that arise from my treatment of the subjects in the first portion of the book. It is my hope that the appendices will answer those questions. For the Christian: It is important to be equipped with responses to the latest arguments being made by atheists, and it is my hope that the appendices will achieve that end.

At the end of each chapter, the common objections made against the material in the chapter are stated, and the appendix containing a response is identified. The reader will also note the questions at the end of each chapter and appendix. These are given in an attempt to help the reader realize whether or not he has followed the line of reasoning given in the chapter or appendix. These questions also serve well in class settings. The material covered in this book could easily serve as the basis of study for at least two quarters of weekly, 45-minute classes.

[NOTE: Introductions for those authors that are liberally quoted throughout the book are only made the first time they appear, to eliminate excess tedium. See the Author index to find the first appearance of each author.]

Jeff Miller

May, 2013

Acknowledgements

Special thanks to the many friends, colleagues, family, and interns who assisted in the editing and publishing of this work.

Introduction

Evolution and Naturalism

If one wishes to explain the existence of the Universe using nature alone—without the help of a supernatural Being—he is a naturalist: an atheist. Evolution, more specifically, **cosmic evolution,** is the naturalist's attempt to explain how everything arrived in the Universe without God. Notice the title of the Web site by Harvard University's astrophysicist Eric Chaisson: "Cosmic Evolution: From Big Bang to Humankind" (2012). Or consider the comments of NASA chief historian, Steven Dick:

> Cosmic evolution begins...with the formation of stars and planetary systems, proceeds...to primitive and complex life, and culminates with intelligence, technology and astronomers...contemplating the universe.... This story of the life of the universe, and our place in it, is known as cosmic evolution (2005).

Evolutionary theories like Darwinian evolution (i.e., the Theory of Evolution) and the Big Bang Theory, taken together, make up cosmic evolution.

Supposedly, such naturalistic theories are the "scientific choice"— the choice based on the scientific evidence. At least that is what the bulk of the scientific community believes today. Those who reject evolutionary theories and subscribe to the Creation model are said to be ignorant, stupid, unenlightened hillbillies who hold to ancient myths and fairytales that have no scientific backing. Well-known evolutionist and professor of zoology at Oxford University, Richard Dawkins, once said, "It is absolutely safe to say that if you meet somebody who claims not to believe in evolution, that person is ignorant, stupid, or insane (or wicked, but I'd rather not consider that)" (1989, p. 7, parenthetical item in orig.). Many Creation scientists today are

1

even expelled from the academic community due to their stance on evolution (cf. Miller, 2011b; Stein and Miller, 2008). If a scientist does not bow to the majority view (i.e., naturalism) of our day, he is marginalized as unscientific and delusional.

This problem comes, in part, due to how naturalists define "science." According to the National Academy of Sciences, "The statements of science must invoke only **natural** things and processes. The statements of science are those that emerge from the application of human intelligence to data obtained from **observation and experiment**" (*Teaching about Evolution...*, 1998, p. 42, emp. added). So according to this modern definition of "science," anything non-natural is excluded. In other words, science must be approached through the **assumption** of naturalism and materialism. Therefore, God is deemed unscientific by this definition (even though the creationist contends that He actually instituted the field of science, see Appendix 6.d), since He is non-natural (i.e., supernatural), non-material, and unobservable. His followers in the creationist community are castigated along with Him.

Evolutionary geologist Robert Hazen, who received his doctoral degree in Earth Science from Harvard University, is a research scientist at the Carnegie Institution of Washington's Geophysical Laboratory and a professor of Earth Science at George Mason University. In his lecture series, *Origins of Life*, Hazen states that he assumes that life came about through a "**natural process**...completely consistent with **natural laws**.... Like other scientists, I rely on the power of **observations and experiments** and theoretical reasoning to understand how the cosmos came to be the way it is" (2005, emp. added). Concerning naturalistic scientists, Richard Lewontin, evolutionary geneticist of Harvard University, unabashedly said:

> Our willingness to accept scientific claims against common sense is the key to an understanding of the real struggle between science and the supernatural. We take the side of science **in spite** of the patent absurdity of some of its constructs, **in spite** of its failure to fulfill many of its extravagant promises of health and life, **in spite** of the tolerance of the scientific community for unsubstantiated just-so stories, because we have a prior commitment, **a commitment to naturalism**. It is not that the methods and institutions of science somehow compel us to

accept a material explanation of the phenomenal world, but, on the contrary, that **we are forced by our *a priori* adherence to material causes** to create an apparatus of investigation and a set of concepts that produce material explanations, no matter how counter-intuitive, no matter how mystifying to the uninitiated. Moreover, **that materialism is absolute, for we cannot allow a Divine Foot in the door** (1997, p. 31, first three emp. in orig.).

So regardless of the evidence, the bulk of today's scientific community has agreed to wipe God and supernatural phenomena out of the definition of "science," not because of the evidence for or against God, but because of the **assumption** of naturalism. But consider: that is a **significant** assumption. It will certainly affect one's results if it is incorrect. The question to be answered in this book is whether or not naturalism is a reasonable assumption.

Not all assumptions in science are "bad" or unreasonable, by any means. If an assumption does not significantly alter the end result, it may be a fair, legitimate assumption. However, the assumption of naturalism significantly alters one's results—yielding completely different answers to important questions than the answers that would be given using an approach without that assumption in place. And further, as this book will highlight, the assumption of naturalism proves to be unreasonable: (1) because it is not in keeping with the evidence, and (2) because it is self-contradictory.

It is time to set the record straight. Today's biased media, as well as the science textbook writers and many college science professors, are "in the tank" for naturalistic theories. So they certainly would not be expected to highlight the bumps—nay, impassable chasms—that exist in the pathway of evolutionary thought. It is evolution—the religion of the naturalist—that is not in keeping with the scientific evidence. The Creation model is consistent with it.

Fundamental Planks of Evolution

There are at least seven fundamental planks that comprise the foundation of naturalistic evolutionary theory (adapted from Gish, et al., 1981; *McLean v....*, 1982):

Seven Fundamental Planks of Cosmic Evolution
1) The Universe (i.e., matter and energy) popped into existence (i.e., it spontaneously generated) or is eternal.
2) Abiogenesis (i.e., spontaneous generation of life from non-life) occurred at some time in the past.
3) Macroevolution (i.e., inter-kind evolution, starting from simple, single-celled organisms and ending with complex life forms, such as humans) accounts for the existence of all present kinds of life forms. [NOTE: Also known as the General Theory of Evolution or Darwinian Evolution]
4) Neo-Darwinism provides the mechanism for macroevolution.
5) Humans and apes have a common ancestor.
6) Uniformitarianism is the appropriate approach to interpreting geologic phenomena.
7) The Universe and life are very old (i.e., billions of years).

In order for atheism and naturalism to be true, each of these planks of evolutionary theory must be true. If any one of these statements can be shown to be unreasonable in light of the evidence, the entire evolutionary model collapses.

The Creation model rests on fundamental planks of its own:

Seven Fundamental Planks of Biblical Creation
1) The Universe was created suddenly by a non-physical (i.e., spiritual) Entity (i.e., God), outside of the boundaries of the physical Universe.
2) Life was also created suddenly by that Being.
3) All present kinds have remained constant since Creation. Microevolution accounts for small-scale changes within very limited parameters (e.g., varieties of dogs, beak sizes, colors, etc.).
4) Neo-Darwinism is insufficient to account for the emergence of present-day kinds from a simple primordial organism. A Creative Power is necessary.
5) Humans and apes have a separate ancestry.
6) Catastrophism is the appropriate approach to interpreting geologic phenomena.

Introduction

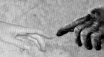

Seven Fundamental Planks of Biblical Creation
7)   The Universe and life are relatively young (i.e., a few thousand years).

The Law of Rationality

What does the **actual evidence** say? Which model is in keeping with that evidence—Creation or evolution? The Law of Rationality in philosophy says one should only draw those conclusions that are warranted by the evidence (Ruby, 1960, pp. 130-131). If a person draws a conclusion that is not in keeping with the evidence, that person is, by definition, being irrational. So if a man born and reared in a primitive country, secluded from all technology, were to run across an automobile for the first time, and from that information drew the conclusion that it is the only car in the Universe, he would be drawing an irrational conclusion. He would lack sufficient evidence to draw that conclusion.

We should be interested in the **evidence**. Our faith in one model or the other should be based, not on blind acceptance of a theory without adequate evidence, not on emotion, not on the view of

> **The Law of Rationality:**
> One should only draw those conclusions that are warranted by the evidence.

the majority, not on prejudice or bias—but the facts. Who would wish to be anything other than sincerely interested in the truth? For several decades, the evolutionary model has held a monopoly on the dissemination of the scientific evidence as it relates to the origin of the Universe. The scientific community today is saturated with naturalists who are biased in their approach towards the question of origins. By and large, it has control of the textbooks, universities, and even the dissemination of information through the media. Though the scientific community proclaims that evolution is the truth—that all the evidence supports it—the real truth is that there is not enough evidence to substantiate evolution. In fact, fundamental scientific evidence refutes naturalism.

We urge you to challenge what you have been told for decades—that evolution is a proven fact; that we owe our origin, not to God, but to a single-celled organism billions of years ago, and millions of years ago to an ape-like creature; that the Bible's Creation story is a fairy-tale—filled with contradictions and scientific blunders. Regardless of how you feel about God, we encourage you to have the fortitude to follow the evidence wherever it leads. The conclusion one reaches on the origins question will have temporal and eternal consequences. If atheistic evolution is not true, then God must exist—and a powerful One at that; One Who can determine one's eternal destiny. Let us look at the evidence. [NOTE: A discussion and refutation of the common issues that today's atheists and skeptics have with the God of the Bible are outside the scope of this book. See Butt, 2010a. Also, see our Web site, www.apologeticspress.org.]

Common Quibbles

- "Evolution is the Scientific Consensus—So You Should Believe it!" [See Appendix 6.a]
- "You Creationists are Unqualified to Speak about Evolution!" [See Appendix 6.b]
- "Science Only Involves Natural—Not Supernatural—Events." [See Appendix 6.c]
- "Science and Religion/God are Incompatible." [See Appendix 6.d]

Review Questions

1) What is a "naturalist" and an "atheist"?
2) What is "cosmic evolution"?
3) How do evolutionists define "science" today?
4) What fundamental assumption made by the scientific community precludes God?
5) What are the seven fundamental planks of cosmic evolution?
6) What does the Law of Rationality state?
7) What are some real life examples of how one might be rational or irrational?

The Laws of Science vs. Evolution

The Laws of Nature—
Immutable and Undeniable

The laws of nature have been discovered through extensive scientific investigation of the natural realm, as scientists have gathered mounds and mounds of evidence, all of which has proven consistently to point to one conclusion. They are, by definition, concluding statements that have been drawn from the scientific evidence, and therefore, are in keeping with the Law of Rationality (Ruby, pp. 130-131). If anything can be said to be "scientific," it is a **law** of science, and to hold to a view or theory that contradicts the laws of science is, by definition, irrational, since such a theory would contradict the evidence from science.

> If anything can be said to be "scientific," it is a law of science.

The laws of science explain how things work in nature at all times—without exception. The *McGraw-Hill Dictionary of Scientific and Technical Terms* defines a scientific law as "a regularity which applies to **all** members of a broad class of phenomena" (2003, p. 1182, emp. added). Notice that the writers use the word "all" rather than "some" or even "most." There are no exceptions to a law of science. Wherever a law is applicable, it has been found to be without exception.

Evolutionists endorse wholeheartedly the laws of science. Robert Hazen, in his lecture series on the origin of life, states, "In this lecture series, I make an **assumption** that life emerged [i.e., spontaneously

generated—JM] from basic raw materials through a sequence of events that was **completely consistent with the natural laws of chemistry and physics**" (Hazen, 2005, emp. added). Even on something as unfounded as postulating the origin of life from non-life—a proposition which flies in the face of all scientific evidence to the contrary (see chapters five through seven)—evolutionists do not wish to resort to calling such a phenomenon an **exception** to the laws of nature. After all, **there are no exceptions** to the laws. Instead, they hope, without evidence, that their claims will prove to be **in keeping** with some elusive, hitherto undiscovered, scientific evidence in the future that will be "completely consistent with the natural laws." [NOTE: Such an approach is the equivalent of brushing aside the mounds of evidence for the existence of gravity in order to develop a theory that asserts that maybe in the past or someday in the future, all humanity will start levitating up from the surface of the Earth. Science has already spoken on that matter, and to postulate such a theory would be unscientific. It would go against the evidence from science. Similarly, science has already spoken on the matter of life from non-life and shown that abiogenesis **does not occur** in nature, according to the Law of Biogenesis (see chapters five through seven). In the words of Hazen, abiogenesis is completely **inconsistent** "with the natural laws of chemistry and physics." And yet he, along with all atheistic evolutionists, continues to promote evolutionary theory in spite of this crucial piece of evidence to the contrary.] Evolutionists believe in the natural laws, even if they fail to concede the import of their implications with regard to atheistic evolution.

Richard Dawkins put his stamp of endorsement on the laws of nature as well. While conjecturing (without evidence) about the possibility of life in outer space, he said, "But that higher intelligence would, itself, had to have come about by some ultimately explicable process. It couldn't have just jumped into existence spontaneously" (Stein and Miller, 2008). Dawkins admits that life could not pop into existence from non-life. But why? Because that would contradict a well-known and respected law of science that is based on mounds of scientific evidence and that has no exception: the Law of Biogenesis (see

chapters five through seven). Of course evolution, to which Dawkins wholeheartedly subscribes, **requires** abiogenesis. However, notice that Dawkins so respects the laws of nature that he cannot bring himself to consciously and openly admit that his theory requires the violation of said law. Self-delusion can be a powerful narcotic.

Famous atheist, theoretical physicist, and cosmologist of Cambridge University, Stephen Hawking, professes to highly revere the laws of science as well. In 2011, he hosted a show on *Discovery Channel* titled, "Curiosity: Did God Create the Universe?" In that show, he said:

> [T]he Universe is a machine governed by principles or laws—laws that can be understood by the human mind. I believe that the discovery of these laws has been humankind's greatest achievement.... But what's really important is that these physical laws, as well as being **unchangeable**, are universal. They apply not just to the flight of the ball, but to the motion of a planet and **everything else in the Universe**. Unlike laws made by humans, the laws of nature **cannot ever be broken**. That's why they are so powerful ("Curiosity...," 2011, emp. added).

According to Hawking, the laws of nature exist, are unbreakable (i.e., without exception), and apply to the entire Universe—not just to the Earth. Evolutionary physicist Victor Stenger submitted that the "basic laws" of science "hold true in the most distant observed galaxy and in the cosmic microwave background, implying that these laws have been valid for over thirteen billion years [NOTE: We do not hold to this deep time supposition—JM]" (2007, p. 115). He went so far as to admit that they are so firmly established as true that "any observation of their violation during the puny human life span would be reasonably termed a miracle" (p. 115).

Again, the atheistic evolutionary community believes in the existence of and highly respects the laws of science (i.e., when those laws coincide with the evolutionist's viewpoints) and would not wish to consciously deny or contradict them. Sadly, they **often** do so when it comes to their beloved atheistic, origin theories. But that admission by the evolutionary community presents a major problem for atheism. Humanist Martin Gardner said:

> Imagine that physicists finally discover all the basic waves and their particles, and all the basic laws, and unite everything in one equation.

We can then ask, "Why that equation?" It is fashionable now to con-jecture that the big bang was caused by a random quantum fluctuation in a vacuum devoid of space and time. But of course such a vacuum is a far cry from nothing. **There had to be quantum laws to fluctuate. And why are there quantum laws?...There is no escape from the superultimate questions: Why is there something rather than nothing, and why is the something structured the way it is?** (2000, p. 303, emp. added).

Spontaneous Generation...of Laws?

Even if Big Bang cosmology were correct, you still can't have a law without a law maker. In "Curiosity: Did God Create the Universe?" Hawking boldly claims that everything in the Universe can be accounted for through atheistic evolution without the need of God. This is untrue, as we have discussed elsewhere (e.g., Miller, 2011a), but notice that Hawking does not even believe that assertion himself. He said, "Did God create the quantum laws that allowed the Big Bang to occur? In a nutshell, did we need a god to set it all up so that the Big Bang could bang?" ("Curiosity..."). He provided no answer to these crucial questions—not even an attempt. And he is not alone. No atheist can provide an adequate answer to those questions.

In the "round table discussion" on the *Discovery Channel* following "Curiosity," titled, "The Creation Question: a Curiosity Conversation," the eminent atheist, theoretical physicist, cosmologist, and astrobiologist of Arizona State University, Paul Davies, noted Hawking's dodge of that question. Concerning Hawking, Davies said,

> In the show, Stephen Hawking gets very, very close to saying, "Well, where did the laws of physics come from? That's where we might find some sort of God." And then he backs away and doesn't return to the subject.... **You need to know where those laws come from. That's where the mystery lies—the laws** ("The Creation Question...," 2011, emp. added).

Astrophysicist and science writer for *New Scientist*, Marcus Chown, wrote:

If the universe owes its origins to quantum theory, then quantum theory must have existed before the universe. So the next question is surely: **where did the laws of quantum theory come from**? "We do not know," admits [cosmologist Alex—JM] Vilenkin. "I consider that an entirely different question." When it comes to the beginning of the universe, in many ways we're still at the beginning (2012, p. 35).

In his book, *The Grand Design*, Hawking tries to submit a way that the Universe could have created itself from nothing in keeping with the laws of nature without God—an impossible concept, to be sure. He says, "Because there is a law like gravity, the universe can and will create itself from nothing" (2010, p. 180). Of course, even if such were possible, he does not explain where the law of gravity came from. A more rational statement would have been the following: "Because there is a law like gravity, the Universe must have been created by God."

Just as all observational evidence says that you cannot have a poem without a poet, a fingerprint without a finger, or a material effect without a cause, a law must be written by someone. But the atheistic community does not believe in the "Someone" Who alone could have written the laws of nature. So the atheist stands in the dark mist of irrationality—holding to a viewpoint that contradicts the evidence. Human observations, without exception, indicate that governing principles or laws originate, not from matter or the random arrangement thereof, but from mind—what we call psychonomygenesis. While the atheist must irrationally hold to apsychonomygenesis, the Christian has no qualms with the existence of the laws of nature. They provide no problem or inconsistency with the Creation model.

Long before the Laws of Thermodynamics were formally articulated in the 1850s and long before the Law of Biogenesis was formally proven by Louis Pasteur in 1864, the laws of science were written in stone and set in place to govern the Universe by the Creator. In the last few chapters of the book of Job, God commenced a speech, humbling Job with the awareness that Job's knowledge and understanding of the workings of the Universe were extremely deficient in comparison with the omniscience and omnipotence of Almighty God. Two of the humbling questions that God asked Job to ponder were, "Do you know the ordinances ["laws"—NIV] of the heavens? Can you set their dominion ["rule"—ESV] over the earth?" (Job 38:33). These were rhetorical questions, and the obvious answer from Job was, "No, Sir." He could not even **know** of all the laws, much less could he **understand** them, and even less could he have written them and established their rule over the Earth. Only a Supreme Being transcendent of the natural Universe would have the power to do such a thing—which was the very point God was making to Job by asking those questions. According to the Creation model and in keeping with the evidence, that Supreme Being is the God of the Bible, Who created everything in the Universe in six literal days, only a few thousand years ago. In the words of the eighteenth century song writer, John Kempthorne, "Praise the Lord, for He hath spoken; worlds His mighty voice obeyed; **laws which never shall be broken**, for their guidance He hath made. Hallelujah! Amen" (1977, #427, emp. added).

Common Quibbles

- "You Creationists Scoff at Theories as Though They are Just Reckless, Uneducated Guesses." [See Appendix 1.a]
- "Couldn't There Have Been (or Be) Exceptions to the Laws of Science?" [See Appendix 1.b]

Review Questions

1) What is a "law" of science?
2) If anything could be said to be "scientific," what would it be?
3) From what are the laws of science the conclusion?
4) True or False? A law of science is a regularity which applies to several members of a broad class of phenomena.
5) Could there be an "exception to the rule" when speaking of a law of science?
6) What did Stephen Hawking say that the laws of nature "cannot ever be"?
7) How is the existence of the laws of science relevant to the Creation/evolution debate?
8) What is a fundamental question that is a mystery to naturalistic scientists?
9) What passage in Job tells us the Author of the ordinances or laws of nature?

Chapter 2

The First and Second Laws of Thermodynamics vs. Evolution

"[T]he principles of thermodynamics have been in existence since the **creation** of the universe" (Cengel and Boles, 2002, p. 2, emp. added). So states a prominent textbook used in schools of engineering across America. Indeed, these principles prove themselves to be absolutely critical in today's science world. Much of the engineering technology available today is based on the foundational truths embodied in the Laws of Thermodynamics. As the writers of one engineering thermodynamics textbook stated: "Energy is a fundamental concept of thermodynamics and one of the most significant aspects of engineering analysis" (Moran and Shapiro, 2000, p. 35). Do these laws have application to the Creation/evolution debate as creationists suggest? What do they actually say and mean?

The word "thermodynamics" originally was used in a publication by Lord Kelvin (formerly William Thomson), the man often called the Father of Thermodynamics because of his articulation of the Second Law of Thermodynamics in 1849 (Cengel and Boles, p. 2). The term comes from two Greek words: *therme*, meaning "heat," and *dunamis*, meaning "force" or "power" (*American Heritage...*, 2000, pp. 558,1795). Thermodynamics can be summarized essentially as the science of energy—including heat, work (defined as the energy required to move a force a certain distance), potential energy, internal energy, and kinetic energy. The basic Laws of Thermodynamics are understood thoroughly today by the scientific community. Thus, the majority of the work with the principles of thermodynamics is done by engineers who simply utilize the already understood principles in their designs. A thorough understanding of the principles of thermo-dynamics which govern our Universe can help an engineer to learn effectively to control the impact of heat and other forms of energy in his designs.

The First and Second Laws of Thermodynamics

Though there are many important thermodynamic principles that govern the behavior of energy, perhaps the most critical principles of significance in the Creation/evolution controversy are the First and Second Laws of Thermodynamics. What are these laws that, not only are vital to the work of an engineer, but central to this debate?

The First Law

The First Law of Thermodynamics was formulated originally by Robert Mayer (1814-1878). He stated: "I therefore hope that I may reckon on the reader's assent when I lay down as an axiomatic truth that, just as in the case of matter, so also in the case of force [the term used at that time for energy—JM], only a transformation but never a

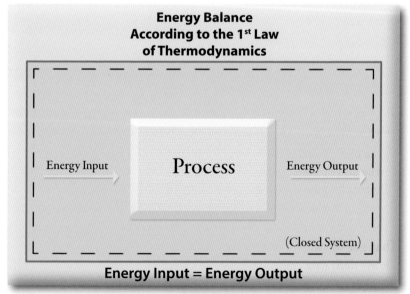

Energy Balance According to the 1st Law of Thermodynamics

Energy Input → Process → Energy Output

(Closed System)

Energy Input = Energy Output

Figure 1

The First and Second Laws of
Thermodynamics vs. Evolution

creation takes place" (as quoted in King, 1962, p. 5). That is, given a certain amount of energy in a closed system, that energy will remain constant, though it will change form (see Figure 1). As evolutionist Willard Young says in defining the First Law, "Energy can be neither created nor destroyed, but can only be converted from one form to another" (1985, p. 8).

This principle, also known as the "conserva-tion of energy principle" (Cengel and Boles, p. 2), can be demonstrated by the burning of a piece of wood. When the wood is burned, it is trans-

> **The First Law of Thermodynamics:**
> "Energy can be neither created nor destroyed, but can only be converted from one form to another."

formed into a different state. The original amount of energy that was present before the burning is still present. However, much of that energy was transformed into a different state—namely, heat. No energy disappeared from the Universe, and no energy was brought into the Universe through burning the wood. Concerning the First Law, Young further explains that

> the principle of the conservation of energy is considered to be **the single most important and fundamental "law of nature"** presently known to science, and is **one of the most firmly established**. Endless studies and experiments have confirmed its validity over and over again under a multitude of different conditions (p. 165, emp. added).

This principle is known to be a **fact** about nature—without exception. One thermodynamics textbook, *Fundamentals of Thermodynamics*, says:

> The basis of every law of nature is experimental evidence, and this is true also of the first law of thermodynamics. Many different experiments have been conducted on the first law, and **every one** thus far has verified it either directly or indirectly. **The first law has never been disproved** (Borgnakke and Sonntag, 2009, p. 116, emp. added).

That is why the *McGraw-Hill Dictionary of Scientific and Technical Terms* defines a scientific law as "a regularity which applies to **all** members of a broad class of phenomena" (p. 1182, emp. added). Recall the words of Stephen Hawking:

But what's really important is that these physical laws, as well as being **unchangeable**, are **universal**. They apply not just to the flight of the ball, but to the motion of a planet and everything else in the Universe. Unlike laws made by humans, the laws of nature **cannot ever be broken**. That's why they are so powerful.... [T]he laws of nature are **fixed** ("Curiosity...," 2011, emp. added).

The Second Law

In the nineteenth century, Lord Kelvin and Rudolph Clausius (1822-1888) separately made findings that became known as the Second Law of Thermodynamics (Suplee, 2000, p. 156). The Second Law builds

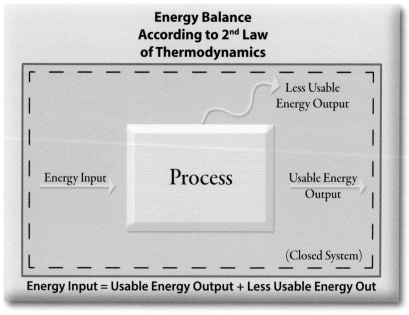

Figure 2

on the First, stating that though there is a constant amount of energy in a given system that is merely transforming into different states, that energy is becoming **less usable**. Extending our aforementioned wood-burning illustration above, after the wood is burned, the total amount of energy is still the same, but has transformed into other energy states. Those energy states (e.g., ash and dissipated heat to the

The First and Second Laws of
Thermodynamics vs. Evolution

environment) are less retrievable and less accessible (see Figure 2). Paul Davies explained it this way:

> [T]he celebrated second law of thermodynamics...says, roughly speaking, that in any change the Universe becomes a slightly more disorderly place; the entropy goes up, the information content goes down. This natural tendency towards disintegration and chaos is evident all around us (1978, 80[1129]:506).

> ## The Second Law of Thermodynamics:
> "[I]n any change the Universe becomes a slightly more disorderly place; the entropy goes up, the information content goes down."

This process is irreversible. Lord Kelvin stated that energy is "irrecoverably lost to man and therefore 'wasted,' although not *annihilated*" (Thomson, 1882, p. 189, italics in orig.). This principle is known as entropy. Simply put, entropy states that nature is tending towards disorder and chaos. Will the paint job on your house maintain its fresh appearance over time? Will your son's room actually become cleaner on its own, or will it tend toward disorder? Even without your son's assistance, dust and decay take their toll. Although work can slow the entropy, it cannot stop it. Renowned evolutionary science writer Isaac Asimov explained:

> Another way of stating the Second Law then is "The universe is constantly getting more disorderly!" Viewed that way we can see the Second Law all about us. We have to work hard to straighten a room, but left to itself it becomes a mess again very quickly and very easily. Even if we never enter it, it becomes dusty and musty. How difficult to maintain houses, and machinery, and our own bodies in perfect working order: how easy to let them deteriorate. In fact, all we have to do is nothing, and everything deteriorates, collapses, breaks down, wears out, all by itself—and that is what the Second Law is all about (1970, p. 6).

Entropy is simply a fact of nature. Entropy can be minimized in this Universe, but it cannot be eradicated. Engineers work to discover ways of minimizing energy loss and maximizing useful energy before it is

forever lost. Thousands of engineering jobs are dedicated to addressing this fundamental fact of the Second Law of Thermodynamics.

Some engineers devote their entire careers to minimizing entropy in the generation of power from energy. All this effort is based on the principles established by the Second Law of Thermodynamics. These principles are established as fact in the scientific community. The *American Heritage Dictionary of the English Language* defines "law" as "a statement describing a relationship observed to be **invariable** between or among phenomena for **all cases** in which the specified conditions are met, [e.g.—JM] *the law of gravity*" (2000, p. 993, emp. added, italics in orig.). Since laws are **invariable**—i.e., unchanging and constant—they have no exceptions. Otherwise, they would not be classified as laws. Tracy Walters, a mechanical engineer working in thermal engineering, observed:

> It has been my experience that many people do not appreciate how uncompromising the Laws of Thermodynamics actually are. It is felt, perhaps, that the Laws are merely general tendencies or possibly only theoretical considerations. In reality, though, the Laws of Thermodynamics are **hard as nails**, and...the more one works with these Laws, the deeper respect one gains for them (1986, 9[2]:8, emp. added).

Evolutionist Jeremy Rifkin stated that "the Entropy Law will preside as the ruling paradigm over the next period of history. Albert Einstein said that it is the premier law of all science; Sir Arthur Eddington referred to it as the 'supreme metaphysical law of the entire universe'" (1980, p. 6). Borgnakke and Sonntag, in *Fundamentals of Thermodynamics*, explain:

> [W]e can say that the second law of thermodynamics (like every other law of nature) rests on experimental evidence. Every relevant experiment that has been conducted, either directly or indirectly, verifies the second law, and **no experiment has ever been conducted that contradicts the second law**. The basis of the second law is therefore experimental evidence (2009, p. 220, emp. added, parenthetical item in orig.).

Another thermal science textbook says, concerning the Second Law of Thermodynamics, "To date, no experiment has been conducted that

The First and Second Laws of
Thermodynamics vs. Evolution

contradicts the second law, and **this should be taken as sufficient proof of its validity**" (Cengel, et al., 2008, p. 266, emp. added).

Implications of the Laws

When used properly, the Laws of Thermodynamics apply directly to the Creation/evolution controversy in precisely the same way they apply in the engineering world today (cf. Miller, 2007). In fact, these foundational truths, utilized daily by the engineering community, have eternally significant, spiritual implications in that they prove that God exists. How so?

If there is no God, the existence of the Universe must be explained without Him. The Big Bang theory claims that all matter in the Universe initially was condensed in a sphere smaller than the size of the period at the end of this sentence. That sphere exploded and supposedly explains why the Universe, according to many cosmologists, appears to be expanding or inflating (see Thompson, et al., 2003, 23[5]:32-34,36-47). Even if the Big Bang were true (and we argue that it is not—cf. Thompson, et al., 2003), this theory offers no explanation for the origin of that sphere. Astrophysicist Marcus Chown, writing in *New Scientist*, said, "The big bang theory...describes the evolution of the universe from a hot, dense state, but it does not say anything about what brought the universe into existence. That still leaves crucial questions unanswered—what happened before the big bang and was there really a beginning?" (2012, p. 33). Evolutionist Alan Guth, a cosmologist and physics professor at M.I.T., admitted that "[i]nflation itself takes a very small universe and produces from it a very big universe. But inflation by itself does not explain where that very small universe came from" (as quoted in Heeren, 1995, p. 148). He further stated, "[A] proposal that the universe was created from empty space is no more fundamental than a proposal that the universe was spawned by a piece of rubber. It might be true, but one would still want to ask where the piece of rubber came from" (Guth, 1997, p. 273). So where could the "rubber" have come from?

Where Did Matter/Energy Come From?

1) Spontaneously generated
2) Eternal
3) Created

Figure 3

The only logical possibilities for the origin of the matter and energy comprising the Universe are that they are responsible for their own existence (i.e., they popped into existence out of nothing—spontaneous generation; or they always existed—eternality) or Someone is responsible for their existence (i.e., they were placed here by something or Someone outside of the Universe—Creation) (see Figure 3).

As a well-known philosopher and evolutionist from the nineteenth century, Herbert Spencer, said, "Respecting the origin of the Universe three verbally intelligible suppositions may be made. We may assert that it is self-existent [i.e., eternal—JM]; or that it is self-created [i.e., spontaneously generated—JM]; or that it is created by an external agency" (1882, p. 30).

Possibility 1: Spontaneous Generation of the Universe

Consider the entire physical Universe as a system consisting of all mass, matter, and energy that exists in the Universe. If one believes in the Big Bang model, the system's boundary would be outside of the blast radius of the Big Bang, or outside of the original cosmic dot that exploded. **Without God** (i.e., Something outside of the bounds of the Universe—Something supernatural), this Universe would have to be a **closed system**. Since our system encompasses the entire Universe, there is no more mass that can cross into our system from the outside, which necessitates our system being closed. If mass, matter, and energy could enter and/or exit the system, the system would be an **open system**. [NOTE: The creationist contends that the Universe **is** an open system, since there is Someone outside of the natural Universe Who

The First and Second Laws of
Thermodynamics vs. Evolution

can cross the boundary and put matter and energy into the system. However, without God, the entire physical Universe as a system logically would **have** to be a **closed** system. Atheists must so believe in order to explain the Universe without God (see Appendix 3.d for a recent response).]

Evolutionary physicist Victor Stenger, in his book, *God: The Failed Hypothesis*, said:

> Conservation of energy [i.e., the First Law—JM] and other basic laws **hold true in the most distant observed galaxy** and in the cosmic microwave background, implying that these laws have been valid for over thirteen billion years [NOTE: We do not hold to this deep time supposition—JM]. Surely any observation of their violation during the puny human life span would be reasonably termed a miracle.... In principle, the creation hypothesis could be confirmed by the direct observation or theoretical requirement that conservation of energy was violated 13.7 billion years ago at the start of the big bang (2007, pp. 115-116, emp. added).

The First Law of Thermodynamics states that in a closed system, the amount of energy present in that system is constant, though it trans-forms into other forms of energy. So, if the Universe as a whole initially contained no mass, matter, or energy, and then all of the mass, matter, and energy in the Universe spontaneously generated, the First Law would have been violated. A miracle would have occurred. Without intervention from an outside force, the amount of mass, matter, and energy in the Universe would have remained constant (unchanged) at **nothing**. According to the scientific evidence, matter/energy could not have originally spontaneously generated. Thus, according to Stenger, the Creation hypothesis is confirmed based on the scientific evidence. The initial creation of energy from nothing amounted to a miracle.

As was mentioned earlier, there are **no exceptions** to laws, or else they would not be laws. The First Law of Thermodynamics has no known exceptions. The Law is accepted as fact by all scientists in general and utilized by engineers in particular. Therefore, the Universe, composed of all mass, matter, and energy, could not have spontaneously generated without violating the exception-less and highly respected First Law of Thermodynamics. The energy level of

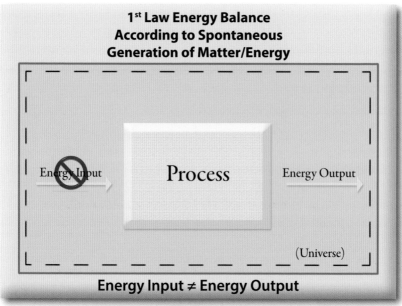

**1st Law Energy Balance
According to Spontaneous
Generation of Matter/Energy**

Energy Input

Process

Energy Output

(Universe)

Energy Input ≠ Energy Output

Figure 4

the Universe would not have been constant. Spontaneous generation would amount to the creation of energy from nothing (see Figure 4). The Universe could not have come into existence without the presence and intervention of a Force outside of the closed system of the entire physical Universe. The Universe therefore must be an **open** system that was created by a non-physical Force (i.e., a Force not composed of mass, matter, and energy) **outside** of the physical boundary of this Universe (above nature, or supernatural) with the capability of bringing it into existence out of nothing. **That Force can be none other than a supernatural God**. To develop a theory that requires the violation of that principle would be against the scientific evidence. It would be unscientific. The evidence from science indicates that the "rubber" of the Universe—matter and energy—could not and cannot spontaneously generate.

Unfortunately, though this truth may be obvious to many, there has been a recent surge of sentiment in the impossible notion that this Universe could have created itself—that something could come from nothing. British evolutionist Anthony Kenny (1980), physics professor from City University in New York, Edward Tryon (1984), and

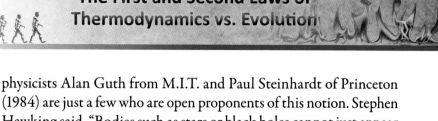

The First and Second Laws of
Thermodynamics vs. Evolution

physicists Alan Guth from M.I.T. and Paul Steinhardt of Princeton (1984) are just a few who are open proponents of this notion. Stephen Hawking said, "Bodies such as stars or black holes cannot just appear out of nothing. But a whole universe can…. Because there is a law like gravity, the universe can and will create itself from nothing" (2010, p. 180). In spite of such baseless, wild claims, the truth still stands. Until the First Law of Thermodynamics ceases to be a fundamental law explaining this Universe, the spontaneous generation of this Universe from nothing is impossible. No wonder Victor Stenger, a proponent of the idea of spontaneous generation, said, "I must admit that there are yet no empirical or observational tests that can be used to test the idea of an accidental origin" (1987, 7[3]:30). According to Stenger, the idea is "speculative" (p. 30). Not solid evidence. Just speculation.

In 1982, Alexander Vilenkin, Director of the Institute of Cosmology at Tufts University, authored an article titled, "Creation of Universes from Nothing." Towards the end of the article, after finishing up the explanation of his argument for how Universes might be able to come from nothing while not contradicting the laws of physics, he made this telling statement: "The only relevant question seems to be whether or not the spontaneous creation of universes is **possible**" (p. 27, emp. added). Relevant question, indeed. Is it really true that individuals who call themselves scientists are actually promoting this far-fetched idea, even though they recognize that it might not even be possible? In other words, "Disregard everything I said up to this point, because regardless of all the fancy scientific jargon and equations, we really still don't know if this is even possible since no one could possibly witness it and there's no proof of it." He even admitted, "The concept of the universe being created from nothing **is a crazy one**" (p. 26, emp. added), and yet he still holds to it and promotes it.

The late, famous evolutionary astronomer Robert Jastrow, founder and former director of the Goddard Institute for Space Studies at NASA, said:

> But the creation of matter out of nothing would **violate** a cherished concept in science—the principle of the conservation of matter and energy [i.e., the First Law of Thermodynamics—JM]—which states

that matter and energy can be neither created nor destroyed. Matter can be converted into energy, and vice versa, but the total amount of all matter and energy in the Universe must remain unchanged forever. **It is difficult to accept a theory that violates such a firmly established scientific fact** (1977, p. 32, emp. added).

According to this famous astronomer, the First Law is "a firmly established scientific fact" that would be violated if the Universe created itself from nothing.

Molecular biologist and philosopher David Berlinski of the Discovery Institute's Center for Science and Culture admitted:

Hot Big Bang cosmology appears to be in **violation** of the first law of thermodynamics. The global energy needed to run the universe has come from nowhere, and to nowhere it apparently goes as the universe loses energy by cooling itself. This contravention of thermodynamics expresses, in physical form, a general philosophical anxiety. Having brought space and time into existence, along with everything else, the Big Bang itself **remains outside any causal scheme** (1998, p. 37, emp. added).

Prominent atheistic writer, David Mills, in his book *Atheist Universe*, wrote, "This something-from-nothing belief is not only false, but **flagrantly violates the law of conservation of mass-energy** [i.e., the First Law of Thermodynamics—JM]" (2006, p. 30, emp. added).

Science studies what occurs in nature, not **super**-nature. In nature, matter and energy can be neither created nor destroyed, but "must remain unchanged **forever**." This is a "firmly established fact." Nothing comes from nothing. If a molecule will not pop into existence from nothing, a sphere containing all of the matter and energy of the entire Universe will most certainly not pop into existence from nothing.

Possibility 2: Eternal Existence of the Universe

Again, considering the entire Universe as a system necessitates that it be a closed system. The Second Law of Thermodynamics states that though energy in a closed system is constant (First Law of Thermodynamics), that energy is transforming into less usable forms of energy (i.e., the Universe is "running down"). This process is irreversible. There is a finite amount of usable energy in the Universe (which explains the

The First and Second Laws of Thermodynamics vs. Evolution

The Universal Timeline

Energy Input ← Finite Amount of Usable Energy → Energy Output

Figure 5

widespread interest in conserving energy). In the Big Bang model, that energy was originally in the cosmic egg that exploded, and now would be found within the blast radius of the original explosion. That usable energy is depleting according to the Second Law. Engineers strive to slow this inevitable depletion of energy, but it cannot be stopped.

If the Universe has always existed (i.e., it is eternal), but there is a finite amount of usable energy, then all usable energy already should be expended (see Figure 5). Yet, usable energy still exists. So, the Universe cannot have existed forever. It had to have a beginning. The eternality of matter would be the equivalent of a system with an energy input and 100% usable energy output (see Figure 6). It would

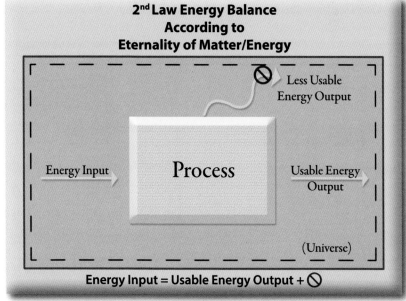

**2ⁿᵈ Law Energy Balance
According to
Eternality of Matter/Energy**

Less Usable Energy Output

Energy Input → Process → Usable Energy Output

(Universe)

Energy Input = Usable Energy Output + ⊘

Figure 6

29

be the equivalent of describing the Universe as a perpetual motion machine—a design that attempts to violate either the First or Second Law of Thermodynamics by, for instance, running forever without an energy input. No such machine has ever been designed, since such a machine would violate the Laws of Thermodynamics. Writing in *Scientific American*, Philip Yam said, "Claims for perpetual-motion machines and other free-energy devices still persist, of course, even though they inevitably turn out to violate at least one law of thermodynamics" (1997, 277[6]:82).

No wonder evolutionists, themselves, have long conceded this truth. In his book, *Until the Sun Dies*, Robert Jastrow stated:

> The lingering decline predicted by astronomers for the end of the world differs from the explosive conditions they have calculated for its birth, but the impact is the same: **modern science denies an eternal existence of the Universe**, either in the past or in the future (1977, p. 30, emp. added).

In his book, *God and the Astronomers*, Jastrow reiterated this truth:

> And concurrently there was a great deal of discussion about the fact that the second law of thermodynamics, applied to the Cosmos, indicates the Universe is running down like a clock. If it is running down, there must have been a time when it was fully wound up.... Now three lines of evidence—the motions of the galaxies, the laws of thermodynamics, the life story of the stars—pointed to one conclusion; all indicated that the Universe had a beginning (1978, pp. 48-49,111).

Evolutionist Kitty Ferguson, an award-winning science writer, agreed. She said, "It's also common knowledge that the universe isn't eternal but had a beginning" (1994, p. 89). Any person who develops a theory that claims that the Universe could be a perpetual motion machine is guilty of contradicting the solid evidence from science. They are being unscientific, and their unscientific mindset has resulted in an unscientific theory.

Possibility 3: The Inevitable Implication

What does the scientific evidence actually say about the matter of origins? Forget baseless speculation, conjecture, hypothesis, and theory—wishful, hopeful thinking that there might be some way to avoid a supernatural explanation. What does the **evidence** say?

To repeat, logically, there are only three possible explanations for the existence of matter in the Universe. Either it spontaneously generated, it is eternal, or it was created by a Being outside of the boundaries of the Universe, not subject to its laws. Atheists use the theory of evolution in an attempt to explain the existence and state of the Universe today. In order for the theory of evolution to be true, thereby accounting for the existence of mankind, **either** all of the mass, matter, and energy of the Universe **spontaneously generated** (i.e., it popped into existence out of nothing), **or** it has **always existed** (i.e., it is eternal.). Without an outside force (a transcendent, omnipotent, eternal, superior Being), no other options for the existence of the Universe are available. However, **as the Laws of Thermodynamics prove**, the spontaneous generation and eternality of matter are logically and scientifically impossible. One and only one possible option remains: the Universe was **created** by the Creator. The scientific evidence points to the existence of God. Bottom line: God designed the Laws of Thermodynamics. Creationists believe them. Engineers use them. Atheists cannot harmonize them with their false theory.

Summary

Evolutionists claim that science and the idea of God are irreconcilable. "Only one of them can be true," they say, "and you cannot prove there is a God." Not all theistic models for the origin of the Universe are in keeping with science. For instance, according to *Enuma Elish*, the Babylonian creation account, the polytheistic Babylonians believed that matter is eternal (Pfeiffer, 1972, p. 226). This notion has been shown to be false. However, although not all Creation models are in harmony with the scientific evidence, one would expect the true Creation model to be in keeping with the evidence. The Laws of Thermodynamics, which science itself recognizes in its explanations of the phenomena in the Universe, were written by the Chief Engineer. As expected, they prove to be in complete harmony with His existence, contrary to the claims of evolutionists. God, Himself, articulated these laws centuries ago in the Bible.

At the very beginning of the Bible, the First Law of Thermodynamics was expressed when Moses penned, "Thus the heavens and the Earth, and all the host of them, **were finished**. And on the seventh day, God **ended** His work which He had done, and He rested on the seventh day from all His work which He had done" (Genesis 2:1-2, emp. added). In Exodus 20:11, Moses wrote, "For in six days, the Lord made the heavens and the earth, the sea, and all that is in them, and rested (i.e., ceased) the seventh day." **Everything** in the Universe was made in six days, and then the Lord stopped creating. Nothing else is coming into existence. After the six days of Creation, the mass, matter, and energy creation process was terminated. As evolutionist Willard Young said regarding the First Law: "Energy can be neither created nor destroyed, but can only be converted from one form to another" (p. 8). The thrust of the First Law of Thermodynamics was expressed in the Bible thousands of years ago, although it was not discovered and formally articulated by scientists until the nineteenth century.

Through the hand of the psalmist, God also stated centuries ago what scientists call the Second Law of Thermodynamics: "Of old You laid the foundation of the Earth, and the heavens are the work of your hands. They will perish, but You will endure; yes, **they will all grow old like a garment**; like a cloak You will change them, and they will be changed. But You are the same, and Your years will have no end" (102:25-27, emp. added). The Universe is wearing out—decaying, like an old shirt: the Second Law of Thermodynamics. Once again, the Creation model is in perfect harmony with science. The evolutionary model fails its thermodynamics test.

The inspired writer wrote in Hebrews 11:3, "By faith we understand that the worlds were framed by the word of God, so that the things which are seen were not made of things which are visible." Paul declared in Acts 14:17, "Nevertheless He did not leave Himself without witness, in that He did good, gave us rain from heaven and fruitful seasons, filling our hearts with food and gladness." The psalmist affirmed, "The heavens declare the glory of God; and the firmament

The First and Second Laws of Thermodynamics vs. Evolution

shows His handiwork" (19:1). Paul assured the Romans, "For since the creation of the world His invisible attributes are clearly seen, being understood by the things that are made, even His eternal power and Godhead, so that they are **without excuse**" (1:20, emp. added). The scientific evidence points to God. There will be no excuse in the end for those who deny it.

In closing this chapter, we return to Lord Kelvin, the Father of Thermodynamics, for fitting final thoughts. In a short public speech in 1903, reported by *The Times* and followed up by an amending letter to the paper by Kelvin, Kelvin said:

> I do not say that, with regard to the origin of life, science neither affirms nor denies Creative Power. **Science positively affirms Creative Power**.... It is not in dead matter that we live and move and have our being [Acts 17:28—JM], but in the creating and directive Power which science compels us to accept as an article of belief.... There is nothing between absolute scientific belief in a Creative Power, and the acceptance of the theory of a fortuitous concourse of atoms.... Forty years ago I asked Liebig, walking somewhere in the country if he believed that the grass and flowers that we saw around us grew by mere chemical forces. He answered, "No, no more than I could believe that a book of botany describing them grew by mere chemical forces".... Do not be afraid of being free thinkers! **If you think strongly enough you will be forced by science to the belief in God**, which is the foundation of all Religion. **You will find science not antagonistic but helpful to Religion** (as quoted in Thompson, 1910, 2:1097-1100, emp. added).

According to the Father of Thermodynamics, atheistic evolutionists are failing to "think strongly enough." Not very politically correct, to be sure, but then again, neither is God: "The fool has said in his heart, 'There is no God'" (14:1).

Common Quibbles

- "Doesn't Quantum Mechanics Prove that the Universe Could Come From Nothing?" [See Appendix 2.a]
- "The Zero Energy Balance in the Universe Allowed it to Pop into Existence." [See Appendix 2.b]
- "The Laws of Thermodynamics Didn't Apply at the Beginning." [See Appendix 2.c]
- "The Universe is Not a Closed System." [See Appendix 2.d]
- "Can't Order come from Disorder on Earth Due to the Sun?" [See Appendix 5.b]

Review Questions

1) What is thermodynamics, and how is it used today?
2) What does the First Law of Thermodynamics say?
3) What does the Second Law of Thermodynamics say?
4) What are the only logical options for the origin of the physical realm?
5) What does the First Law of Thermodynamics imply about the origin of the Universe?
6) What does the Second Law of Thermodynamics imply about the origin of the Universe?
7) If the Universe has always existed, what should be the case today, according to the Second Law?
8) What Bible verses state the essentials of the First and Second Laws?
9) What conclusion can be drawn about the origin of the Universe based on the Laws of Thermodynamics?

Chapter 3

The Law of Causality vs. Evolution

The Law of Cause and Effect states that every material effect must have an adequate antecedent or simultaneous cause. A paper clip is not going to provide sufficient gravitational pull to cause a tidal wave. There must be an adequate cause for the tidal wave, like a massive, offshore, underwater earthquake ("Tsunamis," 2000, p. 1064). Leaning against a mountain will certainly not cause it to topple over. Jumping up and down on the ground will not cause an earthquake. If a chair is not placed in an empty room, the room will remain chair-less. If matter was not made and placed in the Universe, the Universe would not exist. There must be an adequate antecedent or simultaneous cause for every material effect. Perhaps the Law of Cause and Effect seems

> **The Law of Causality:**
> Every material effect must have an adequate antecedent or simultaneous cause.

intuitive to most, but common sense tends to dissolve with many when God is brought into the discussion.

Causality and History

The Law of Cause and Effect, or Law/Principle of Causality, has been investigated and recognized for millennia. In *Phaedo*, written by Plato in 360 B.C., an "investigation of nature" is spoken of concerning causality, wherein "the causes of **everything**, why **each thing** comes into being and why it perishes and why it exists" are discussed (Plato,

1966, 1:96a-b, emp. added). Plato recognized the fact of causality. In 350 B.C., Aristotle contributed more to the causality discussion by stipulating that causes can be "spoken of in four senses": material, formal, efficient, and final (Aristotle, 2009, 1[3]). Moving forward two millennia in no way deterred humanity from recognizing the truth of causality. In 1781, the renowned philosopher Immanuel Kant wrote concerning the Principle of Causality in his *Critique of Pure Reason* that "according to the Law of Causality," "everything that happens presupposes a previous condition, which it follows with absolute certainty, in conformity with a rule.... **All changes** take place according to the **law of the connection of Cause and Effect**" (2008, pp. 120, 218, emp. added). In the nineteenth century, German medical scientist and Father of Cellular Pathology, Rudolf Virchow, affirmed that "[e]verywhere there is mechanistic process only, with the **unbreakable necessity of cause and effect**" (1858, p. 115, emp. added).

Fast forwarding another century, our understanding of the world still did not cause the law to be discredited. In 1934, W.T. Stace, professor of philosophy at Princeton University, in *A Critical History of Greek Philosophy*, wrote:

> Every student of logic knows that this is **the ultimate canon of the sciences**, the foundation of them all. If we did not believe the truth of causation, namely, everything which has a beginning has a cause, and that in the same circumstances the same things invariably happen, all the sciences would at once crumble to dust. In **every scientific investigation** this truth is assumed (1934, p. 6, emp. added).

The truth of causality is so substantiated that it is taken for granted in scientific investigation. It is "assumed."

This principle is not some idea that can simply be brushed aside without consideration. If the Law of Causality were not in effect, science could not proceed—it would "crumble to dust," since by its very nature, it involves gathering evidence and testing hypotheses in order to find **regularities** in nature. The goal of scientific experimentation is to determine what will happen (i.e., what will be the **effect**) if one does certain things (i.e., initiates certain **causes**). If there were no relationship between cause and effect, then nothing could be

taken for granted. One day gravity may be in effect, and the next day it may not, and there would be no point in studying it, since it might be different tomorrow. There would be no such thing as a "scientific law," since there would be no such thing as a "regularity," which is fundamental to the definition of a law of science.

Moving into the twentieth century, the Law of Cause and Effect still had not been repealed. In 1949, Albert Einstein, in *The World as I See It*, under the heading "The Religiousness of Science," wrote, "But the scientist is possessed by the sense of **universal causation**" (2007, p. 35, emp. added). In *The Encyclopedia of Philosophy*, renowned American philosopher and professor Richard Taylor wrote, "Nevertheless, it is hardly disputable that the idea of causation is not only indispensable in the common affairs of life but in **all** applied sciences as well" (1967, p. 57, emp. added).

Even today, when scientific exploration has brought us to unprecedented heights of knowledge, the age old Law of Causality cannot be denied. Today's dictionaries define "causality" as:

- "the principle that **nothing** can happen without being caused" (*Collins English Dictionary...*, 2009, emp. added).

- "the principle that **everything** has a cause" (*Concise Oxford English Dictionary*, 2008, emp. added).

The National Academy of Science's guidebook, *Teaching about Evolution and the Nature of Science*, says, "One goal of science is to understand nature. 'Understanding' in science means relating one natural phenomenon to another and recognizing **the causes and effects of phenomena**.... Progress in science consists of the development of better explanations for the **causes** of natural phenomena" (1998, p. 42, emp. added). The National Academy of Science, though entirely naturalistic in its approach to science, recognizes causality to be fundamental to the nature of science. It is not, and cannot rationally be, denied—except when necessary in order to prop up a deficient worldview. Its ramifications have been argued for years, but after the dust settles, the Law of Cause and Effect still stands unscathed, having weathered the trials thrust upon it for thousands of years.

The Law of Causality—A Problem for Atheists

The Law of Causality is fundamental to science, and yet it stands in the way of the bulk of today's scientific community due to its flawed definition of "science." In an interview in 1994, Robert Jastrow explained:

> As Einstein said, scientists live by their faith in causation, and the chain of cause and effect. Every effect has a cause that can be discovered by rational arguments. And this has been a very successful program, if you will, for unraveling the history of the universe. **But it just fails at the beginning**.... So time, really, going backward, comes to a halt at that point. Beyond that, that curtain can never be lifted.... **And that is really a blow at the very fundamental premise that motivates all scientists** (as quoted in Heeren, 1995, p. 303, emp. added).

The scientific community today, by and large, incorrectly defines "science" in such a way that anything supernatural cannot be considered "scientific," and therefore science "fails" in certain areas. Only natural phenomena are deemed worthy of being categorized "science." According to the definition, if something cannot be empirically observed and tested, it is not "scientific." [NOTE: The naturalistic community contradicts itself on this matter, since several fundamental planks of evolutionary theories are unnatural—they have never been observed and all scientific investigation has proven them to be impossible (e.g., spontaneous generation of life and the laws of science, macroevolution, etc., see Appendix 6.c).] One result of this flawed definition is highlighted by Jastrow, himself, in the above quote. Contrary to Jastrow's statement, the laws of science, by definition, do not "fail." They have no known exceptions. So, it would be unscientific to claim, without conclusive evidence in support of the claim, that a law has failed.

This leaves atheistic evolutionists in a quandary when trying to explain how the effect of the infinitely complex Universe could have come about unscientifically—without a cause. Three decades ago, Jastrow wrote:

> The Universe, and everything that has happened in it since the beginning of time, are a grand effect without a known cause. An effect without

a known cause? That is not the world of science; it is a world of witch-craft, of wild events and the whims of demons, a medieval world that science has tried to banish. As [naturalistic—JM] scientists, what are we to make of this picture? I do not know (1977, p. 21).

Again, when Jastrow says that there is no "known cause" for every-thing in the Universe, he is referring to the fact that there is no known **natural** cause. If atheism were true, there must be a natural explanation of what caused the Universe. Scientists and philosophers recognize that there must be a cause that would be sufficient to bring about matter and the Universe—and yet no natural cause is known. By implication those who hold to naturalism cling to a blind faith in it. The *McGraw-Hill Dictionary of Scientific and Technical Terms* says that "causality," in physics, is "the principle that an event cannot precede its cause" (2003, p. 346). However, the atheist must concede that in order for his claim to be valid, the effect of the Universe did not **precede** its cause. Instead, it actually came about **without it!** Such a viewpoint is hardly in keeping with science.

The Law of Causality—A Friend to Creationists

Instead of flippantly disregarding the truth of the Law of Causality because it contradicts naturalistic theories, why not recognize that the highly respected, exception-less Law of Causality is not the prob-lem? Why not recognize the fact that naturalistic theories, such as the Theory of Evolution and the Big Bang Theory, are simply not in harmony with science on a fundamental level? Why not consider an option that does not contradict the Law? If one were to follow the evidence wherever it leads, rather than defining God out of science, one is led to the unavoidable conclusion that there must be Someone **super**-natural that caused the Universe to be. If every material (i.e., natural) effect must have a cause, then the ultimate Cause of the Universe must be supernatural.

Every material effect must have an adequate antecedent or simulta-neous cause. Notice that creationists have absolutely no problem with the truth articulated by this God-ordained law from antiquity. The

Bible, in essence, articulated the Law of Causality millennia ago when in Hebrews 3:4 it says that "every house is built by someone, but He who built all things is God." A house must have a cause—namely, a builder. It will not build itself. Scientifically speaking, according to the Law of Cause and Effect, there had to be a Cause for the Universe. That Cause had to exist before or simultaneous with its effect, and had to be adequate enough to produce its effect. The only book on the planet which contains characteristics that prove its production to be above human capability is the Bible (see Butt, 2007), and the God spoken of therein is its Author (2 Timothy 3:16-17). In the very first verse of the inspired material He gave to humans, He articulated with authority and clarity that He is the Cause Who brought about the Universe and all that is in it. "In the beginning, God created the heavens and the Earth" (Genesis 1:1).

Emile Borel was a famous French mathematician for whom the Borel lunar crater was named (O'Connor and Robertson, 2008). He once said concerning the amazing human brain that is able to author works of literature, "Now the complexity of that brain must therefore have been even richer than the particular work to which it gave birth" (1963, p. 125). The effect of the brain's existence, like a work of literature, must have an adequate cause. In the same way, we know that the infinite Mind behind the creation of this infinitely complex Universe had to be, and was, more than adequate for the task of bringing it all into existence (Revelation 19:6).

The Law of Causality
vs. Evolution

Common Quibbles

- "If Everything Has a Cause, What Caused God?" [See Appendix 3.a]
- "No Cause for the Universe is Necessary!" [See Appendix 3.b]

Review Questions

1) What does the Law of Causality state?
2) If every material effect must have a cause, the initial material effect must have had what kind of cause?
3) According to the Law of Causality, what does the scientific evidence indicate that the Universe must have had?
4) What Bible passage states the thrust of the Law of Causality?

Chapter 4

The Laws of Probability vs. Evolution

Probability and Science

A typical misconception about science is that it can tell us what will **definitely** happen now or in the future given enough time, or what would **certainly** have happened in the past, given enough time. The truth is, science is limited in that it does not grant absolute truth, but only yields degrees of probability or likelihood based on previously gathered results. Science observes the Universe, records evidence, and strives to draw conclusions about what has happened in the past, is happening now, and what will **potentially** happen in the future, given the current state of scientific knowledge—which is often times woefully incomplete, and even inaccurate. The late, prominent evolutionist and paleontologist George Gaylord Simpson discussed the nature of science and probability several years ago in the classic textbook, *Life: An Introduction to Biology*, stating:

> We speak in terms of "acceptance," "confidence," and **"probability,"** not "proof." If by proof is meant the establishment of eternal and absolute truth, open to no possible exception or modification, then proof has no place in the natural sciences. Alternatively, proof in a natural science, such as biology, must be defined as the attainment of a **high degree of confidence** (Simpson and Beck, 1965, p. 16, emp. added).

In other words, science observes and attempts to answer for mankind such things as: what could have happened in the past; what most likely happened; what is probably happening now; what could happen in the future; or what will likely happen in the future. Science does not

necessarily tell us what will **certainly** always be or has always been the case. Rather, it tells us what has been **observed** to be the case and attempts to tell us what will almost certainly always be the case, without exception, and which coincides with logic, intuition, and mathematics. Probability is intimately intertwined with science. Mark Kac, famous mathematician and professor at Cornell and Rockefeller Universities, said: "Probability is a cornerstone of **all** the sciences, and its daughter, the science of statistics, enters into **all** human activities" (as quoted in Smith, 1975, p. 111, emp. added).

Many evolutionists understand the significance of probability in science and yet go too far in their use of it, presumptuously claiming that probability can do more than it is capable of doing. These assert that anything—no matter how far-fetched—will inevitably happen, given enough time, as long as it does not have a probability of zero. Supposedly, objects will pop into existence, and eventually, those things will come to life and transform into humans. Many evolutionists have long cited the principles of probability in an effort to support such unscientific dogmas (e.g., Erwin, 2000). Cosmologist Alex Vilenkin, concerning elements of the Big Bang and quantum theory, said, "Although the probability may be very small, since an infinite amount of time is available, it is **inevitable**" (as quoted in Chown, 2012, p. 35, emp. added). As far back as 1954, evolutionist George Wald, professor at Harvard University and Nobel Prize winner in physiology and medicine, writing in *Scientific American* concerning the origin of life on Earth, penned the words:

> However improbable we regard this event, or any of the steps it involves, **given enough time**, it will almost certainly happen at least once. And for life as we know it, once may be enough. **Time is the hero of the plot**.... Given so much time, **the impossible becomes possible, the possible becomes probable, and the probable becomes virtually certain.** One has only to wait; **time itself performs miracles** (p. 48, emp. added).

There are at least four problems with such assertions about the laws of probability.

The Single Law of Chance

The first problem with the assertion of evolutionary inevitability due to probability is implied by the work of the previously mentioned, renowned French mathematician Emile Borel. In 1962, Borel discussed in depth the law of probability known as the Single Law of Chance—a law that he said "is extremely simple and intuitively evident, though rationally undemonstrable" (p. 2). This principle states that "events whose probability is extremely small never occur" (1965, p. 57). He further stated that we "at least...must act, in all circumstances, as if they were *impossible*" (1962, p. 3, italics in orig.). The law, he said, applies to

> the sort of event, which, though its *impossibility* may not be rationally demonstrable, is, however, so unlikely that no **sensible** person will hesitate to declare it *actually impossible*. If someone affirmed having observed such an event we would be sure that he is **deceiving** us or has himself been the victim of a fraud (1962, p. 3, italics in orig., emp. added).

To clarify the meaning of "extremely small" probabilities, he defined different categories comprised of events in which the probabilities are so small that they are "practically negligible," including events from the perspective of the individual human, the cumulative probability of the entire Earth, and from the perspective of the entire Universe (1965, p. 57).

The Single Law of Chance: Events whose probabilities are extremely small never occur.

In his discussion on the probabilities of certain cosmic events and starting with commonly held human beliefs concerning negligible events, he argues convincingly using mathematical calculations that reasonable human beings consider probabilities of chance cosmic events that fall below one in 10^{45} to be negligible (1965, p. 59). In other words, if the probability of a certain event happening in the Universe is less than one in 10^{45} (i.e., a one with 45 zeros after it), human beings intuitively categorize that event as so unlikely that we consider it to be an **impossible** event.

What does that have to do with the Creation/evolution debate? If there is no God, then at some point in the past, life had to spring into existence from non-living materials. Several years ago, evolutionist Harold Morowitz of Yale, and currently professor of biology and natural philosophy at George Mason University, estimated the probability of the formation of the smallest and simplest living organism to be one in $10^{340,000,000}$ (1970, p. 99). A few years following Morowitz's calculations, the late, renowned evolutionist Carl Sagan made his own estimation of the chance that life could evolve on any given single planet: one in $10^{2,000,000,000}$ (1973, p. 46)! Note also that these calculations were made before the last several decades have revealed with even more clarity the complexity of life (cf. Deweese, 2010). These probability estimations for the formation of life, made by evolutionists themselves, are, of course, so far under the limit articulated for cosmic events by the Single Law of Chance that we must respond in shock, rather than humor, at the big lie that has been perpetrated on the world at large by so many in the scientific community in thrusting naturalistic evolution on the masses. According to the Single Law of Chance, belief in abiogenesis is not "sensible." Those who believe it have been duped or are "deceiving us."

The late, distinguished British astronomer Sir Fred Hoyle once said regarding evolution: "[T]he chance that higher forms have emerged in this way is comparable with the chance that a tornado sweeping through a junk-yard might assemble a Boeing 747 from the materials therein" (1981b, 294:105). He further stated:

> At all events, anyone with even a nodding acquaintance with the Rubik cube will concede the near-impossibility of a solution being obtained by a blind person moving the cubic faces at random. Now imagine 10^{50} blind persons each with a scrambled Rubik cube, and try to conceive of the chance of them all **simultaneously** arriving at the solved form. You then have the chance of arriving by random shuffling of **just one of the many biopolymers on which life depends**. The notion that not only biopolymers but the operating programme of a living cell could be arrived at by chance in a primordial organic soup here on the Earth is evidently **nonsense of a high order** (1981a, 92:527, 1st emp. in orig.).

Borel's Single Law of Chance certainly lays plain the impossibility and incredibility of the evolutionary proposition. However, Borel, being an evolutionist, tried to distance himself from the implications of his findings and their application to the spontaneous emergence of life by noting that the laws of chance do "not **seem** possible to apply" to some evolutionary events (1963, p. 125, emp. added). Why? He explained:

> [I]t is generally held that living beings are the result of a slow process of evolution, beginning with elementary organisms, and that this process of evolution involves certain properties of living matter that prevent us from asserting that the process was accomplished in accordance with the laws of chance (1963, p. 125).

In other words, evolutionary processes cannot be considered a succession of random, chance events. Instead, it seems that they are considered **intentional** events—that somehow occur without intention, since intention requires a mind. Since non-living matter has no mind of its own, the progression of events that would have to occur to lead to the optimal arrangement of that matter to allegedly bring about life would have to be just that—a succession of random, chance events.

Notice that while incorrectly making the assertion that the laws of chance do not apply to evolution, he tacitly acknowledged the fact that the evolutionary model is worse off than before he spoke. Evolution would actually require **multiple, successive** random events taking place gradually over time in order to bring even the pre-living "organism" to a place in which life could allegedly burst into existence. And as if to further drive the tombstone into the grave, according to Borel, himself, "[i]t is repetition that creates improbability" (1962, p. 3). Applying, that principle to the evolutionary model is telling. Such almost endless successive random events would actually create even **more** of a problem for evolution. "[I]t is their [the successive repetition of improbable events leading towards significant complexity—JM] almost indefinite repetition that creates improbability and rightly seems to us **impossible**" (1962, pp. 3-4, emp. added). After all of these successive evolutionary events leading towards life, the final random, chance event in which all the circumstances happen to be "just right" to bring about the jump from non-life to life is so improbable, **according to the evolutionists themselves**, that the

Single Law of Chance would consider the event **impossible** and not worthy of human attention. [NOTE: I am not suggesting that it is possible for life to be spontaneously created from non-life, no matter what the circumstances or arrangements of matter may be. I am only noting the implications of the evolutionists' own arguments and their application to the laws of science.]

Kolmogorov's First Axiom

A second problem exists with the assertion that macroevolution will inevitably happen, given enough time, as long as it does not have a probability of zero—namely Kolmogorov's First Axiom. Statements like Wald's are contingent on the idea that there is a probability of evolution occurring, although extremely minute. However, if a zero probability exists, it will not matter how much time is allotted. The event will not occur since it has a zero probability.

Several of the events that are necessary in order for the theory of evolution and the Big Bang Theory to be true, indeed, **have** a probability of zero, according to the scientific evidence. For instance, before the alleged Big Bang, a small, condensed sphere supposedly existed that was comprised all of the matter in the Universe (cf. Thompson, et al., 2003). Where did it come from? Consider for a moment the spontaneous generation of that sphere of matter. Its appearance and subsequent organization, being a random, chance event, would fall under the guidelines of the Single Law of Chance as well. Unfortunately for evolutionists, since all scientific evidence indicates that matter cannot spontaneously generate (according to the First Law of Thermodynamics; see chapter two), the probability of such an event would be much less than the "one in 10^{45}" barrier set by the Single Law of Chance—namely, **zero**.

Also, what proof is available that leads to the idea that life could spontaneously generate (i.e., abiogenesis)? What scientific evidence is available that would lead to the idea that abiogenesis has a probability of anything but **zero**? Speculation abounds concerning the sequence of events that could cause precisely the right conditions for

it to occur. However, there is zero scientific evidence to support the idea that it could happen even if those improbable conditions were ever in effect. In actuality, the scientific evidence is not "neutral" on the matter, as though there is no evidence for or against abiogenesis. Rather, the scientific evidence is not only unsupportive of abiogenesis, but all experimental scientific results are contrary to it! The experiments of renowned nineteenth century scientist Louis Pasteur long ago eliminated the possibility of the spontaneous generation of life. Recognition of the well-respected law of science known as the Law of Biogenesis (i.e., in nature, life comes only from life and that of its kind) drove the nails into its coffin (see chapters five through seven).

Consider that probabilities simply highlight trends that have been observed to occur in the past by observing the natural order—the Universe. So, if there is an event that has never been shown to be able to occur in nature, then the event stands as having a zero probability. One cannot simply wave his hand and magically designate a probability to an event that science has repeatedly proven not to occur. Science has not shown that abiogenesis occurs one in three million tries. That would at least give the event a probability, though remote. However, that is not what scientific investigation has resulted in. There is **no evidence** to support a probability of anything other than zero for several evolutionary events. So, the whole question of evolution is not really even one of improbability, but **impossibility**. How can one calculate the probability of something happening for which there is zero evidence that such a thing can even occur? Chance applies only to events or circumstances wherein possibility is present.

This insight leads to a fundamental truth. The late, renowned Russian mathematician Andrey Kolmogorov is perhaps most remembered for his work in probability theory ("Andrey Nikolayevich...," 2013). According to the laws of probability, specifically Kolmogorov's First Axiom, when the probability of an event is zero, the event is called an "**impossible event**" (Gubner, 2006, p. 22, emp. added). Since

Kolmogorov's First Axiom:
Events whose probabilities are zero are "impossible events."

several events that are necessary in order for the theory of evolution and the Big Bang Theory to be true have a probability of zero, according to the laws of probability, these atheistic theories are **impossible**.

Given Enough Time

Recall the words of George Wald of Harvard: "However improbable we regard this event, or any of the steps it involves, given enough time, it will almost certainly happen at least once" (1954, p. 48). We have already seen that abiogenesis, a fundamental assumption of evolutionary theory (cf. Hazen, 2005) and the subject of this quote, does not even belong in a discussion on probability since it is an impossible event. But there is another fundamental issue with such a statement. Even if Darwinian evolution did indeed have a minute possibility of occurring, we simply are not "given enough time" for macroevolution to have occurred. We at Apologetics Press have documented this fact time and time again (cf. Jackson, 1983; Thompson, 2001). Years ago, in his article "The Young Earth," the late, hydraulic and civil engineer Henry Morris, of the University of Minnesota and Southwestern Louisiana University, where he was the Head of the Civil Engineering Department, listed 76 scientific dating techniques, based on standard evolutionary assumptions, which contradict the assertions of evolutionary geologists and indicate that the Earth is relatively young (Morris, 1974). Donald DeYoung documented extensive, compelling evidence for a young Earth as well, in the book *Thousands...Not Billions* (2005). This fact alone dispels the preposterous contention that we are the descendants of ape-like creatures.

Probability and Causal Power

Further, even if there were **not** a probability of zero when it comes to macroevolution, that possibility would not guarantee that it would happen, contrary to Wald's assertion. It is important to note, as was discussed at the beginning of this chapter, that probabilities do not guarantee that an event will or will not happen, regardless of how

much time is allotted. Theologians Sproul, Gerstner, and Lindsley correctly observed:

> The fact is, however, we have a no-chance chance creation. We must erase the "1" which appears above the line of the "1" followed by a large number of zeroes. What are the real chances of a universe created by chance? Not a chance. Chance is incapable of creating a single molecule, let alone an entire universe. Why not? Chance is **no thing**. It is not an entity. It has no being, no power, no force. It can effect nothing for it has no causal power within it, it has no **it**ness to be within. Chance...is a word which describes mathematical possibilities which, by a curious slip of the fallacy of ambiguity, slips into discussion as if it were a real entity with real power, indeed, supreme power, the power of creativity (1984, p. 118, emp. in orig.).

We certainly agree. There is only one causal Power capable of creating the Universe, and there is certainly nothing random about Him.

Summary

Recall what Borel said of events prohibited under the Single Law of Chance—that **sensible** humans "must act, in all circumstances, as if they were *impossible*" (1962, p. 3, italics in orig.). Unfortunately, so many scientists today do not act sensibly. They do not follow this simple and intuitive truth when it comes to the matter of origins. Rather, they hold to the impossible, pouring thousands of hours and billions of dollars into researching it, writing on it, speaking on it, thrusting it into the minds of people of all ages, and demonizing anyone who contradicts them. They, themselves, admit that the spontaneous generation of life from non-life has never been observed and that the odds are shockingly against it. The idea is "nonsense of a high order" (Hoyle, 1981a, 92:527). Yet, since they start with the presumptuous assumption that there is no God, they believe the existence of life is proof enough that spontaneous generation occurred.

But if the scientific evidence is so strongly against abiogenesis, how can it be considered scientific? Even if there was a 0.0000...1% chance that macroevolution could happen, why would a scientist stake his name and entire career on such astronomical, outrageous odds when, if biased assumptions are dropped, there is a much more plausible explanation for the origin of this Universe? Prominent evolutionist, Richard Dawkins, himself admitted, "The more statistically improbable a thing is, the less we can believe that it just happened by blind chance. Superficially the **obvious alternative** to chance is an intelligent Designer" (1982, p. 130, emp. added). We certainly agree, and sadly, the implication of that alternative is the very reason so many people irrationally hold onto impossibilities—the intelligent Designer has expectations to which this generation refuses to submit.

Nevertheless, in the words of Emile Borel:

> When we calculated the probability of reproducing by mere chance a work of literature, in one or more volumes, we certainly observed that, if this work was printed, it must originally have emanated from a human brain. Now the complexity of that brain must therefore have been even **richer** than the particular work to which it gave birth (1963, p. 125, emp. added).

And if we might add another line to Borel's statement: "And further, the complexity of the Mind that gave birth to that brain must be truly incomprehensible!"

Common Quibbles

- Since Science is Intertwined with Probability, Though Unlikely, Couldn't the Laws of Science have been Broken in the Past, Allowing Naturalism to be Possible? [See Appendix 1.b]

Review Questions

1) How are probability and science intimately intertwined?

2) According to evolutionists, as long as an event does not have a probability of zero, it will happen, given enough time. What are some of the problems with that statement?

3) Emile Borel stated what law of probability, and what does it say?

4) If there is no evidence that an event can occur, what probability does it have?

5) What does Kolmogorov's First Axiom state?

6) Contrary to the deep time supposition of atheistic evolution, what do many dating techniques indicate about the age of the Universe?

7) What do probabilities not have that highlight the fact that they cannot guarantee something will or will not happen?

Science vs. Evolution

Chapter 5

The Law of Biogenesis vs. Evolution [Part I]

Introduction

It is highly unlikely that a high school or college biology student will learn about the gaping chasms that exist in evolutionary theory: chasms over which scientists have no crossing bridges even designed, much less constructed. The existence of these chasms causes the entire theory of evolution to collapse, and that is precisely the reason these chasms are not broadcasted in school curricula: chasms such as the origin of matter as well as the laws which govern it (see chapters one and two for more on these chasms). At least two of these chasms exist due to the existence of the irrefutable, highly respected Law of Biogenesis (Clifford and DiGiovanni, 2010; Carlson, 2008; "Cell Theory and Microscopes...," 2013; Simmons, 2007; not to be confused with Haeckel's false "Biogenetic Law"). This law states that in nature, life comes only from life and that of its own kind.

The Earth is filled with non-living matter. The Earth also abounds with living creatures. The difference between the two is hardly insignificant. Human beings cannot create life, though many attempts have been made (e.g., Wong, et al., 2000; Miller and Levine, 1991, pp.

> **Law of Biogenesis:**
> In nature, life comes only from life and that of its kind.

343-344; Hartgerink, et al., 2001; for refutations, see Houts, 2007; Thompson and Harrub, 2003). There is no evidence that anyone has **ever** been able to bring about life from non-life in nature (i.e., excluding **supernatural** occurrences during the miraculous periods of human history; e.g., Peter in Acts 9:32-41; Elisha in 2 Kings 4:17-37; and Elijah in 1 Kings 17:17-24). The jump from non-life to life is no trivial matter.

So, how did life originate? Entire worldviews are built upon the answer to that question. There are ultimately only two possibilities. Years ago, George Wald recognized as much, stating that "the reasonable view was to believe in spontaneous generation; the only alternative, to believe in a single, primary act of supernatural creation. There is no third position" (1954, p. 46). There are only two options for the origin of life. It was created, or it created itself. Robert Jastrow said, "**either** life was created on the earth by the will of a being outside the grasp of scientific understanding, **or** it evolved on our planet spontaneously, through chemical reactions occurring in nonliving matter lying on the surface of the planet" (1977, pp. 62-63, emp. in orig.).

The biblical creationist asserts that life originally came directly from God. Concerning human beings, Genesis 2:7 says, "And the Lord God formed man of the dust of the ground, and breathed into his nostrils the breath of life; and man became a living being." [NOTE: This view, incidentally, is in contradiction with the theistic evolutionist's attempt to harmonize the Bible's story of origins with evolutionary theory, which portrays God as giving life to the original cell on Earth. Then, that cell, in accordance with evolutionary theory, evolved from creature to creature until humans came on the scene. God, in that portrait, never "breathed" life into man's "nostrils" at all, but rather, into the "nostrils" of a noseless cell. See Appendix 6.f for a brief discussion on theistic evolution and Thompson, 2000 for an in-depth study.] The atheist asserts that life created itself, a belief known as biopoiesis. The *Encyclopaedia Britannica* defines "biopoiesis," also called spontaneous generation, abiogenesis, and autogenesis (*McGraw-Hill Dictionary...*, 2003, p. 3), as "a process by which living organisms are thought to develop from nonliving matter, and the **basis** of a theory on the origin of life on Earth [i.e., the theory of evolution—JM]" (2011, emp. added). According to naturalistic theories, in essence, once upon a time, there was a dead rock that oozed non-living, primeval, prebiotic, organic soup (Lahav, 1999; Miller and Levine, 1991; Hoyle and Wickramasinghe, 1978). One day, lightning struck, and that soup came to life.

The atheistic evolutionist must hold to a belief in abiogenesis in order for his position to appear tenable. It is a fundamental premise of naturalistic evolution. If biopoiesis did not occur, atheistic evolution cannot occur. This fact was recognized as far back as 1960, when noted physiologist and zoologist G.A. Kerkut published *The Implications of Evolution*. Therein he listed seven **non-provable assumptions** upon which evolution is based. "The first assumption is that non-living things gave rise to living material, i.e., spontaneous generation occurred" (p. 6). In spite of the admission that evolution is based on non-provable assumptions, many today in the evolutionary community boldly assert that their theory is a scientific fact. However, the unbiased observer must ask: what does the scientific evidence actually have to say about the origin of life?

The History of the Law of Biogenesis

Francesco Redi (1626-1697)

Understanding life at the microscopic level due to the state of technology today might make the work of Italian scientist, Francesco Redi, seem trivial to many. Before achieving the microscopic viewing capabilities we have today, however, some things we take for granted were not so apparent. Long ago, the Greeks believed that abiogenesis was common (Balme, 1962). This belief continued to be the dominant position for millennia. Even as late as 300 years ago, it was standard belief in the scientific community that

life commonly and spontaneously arose from non-life. For instance, it was believed that when a piece of meat rotted, it "spontaneously" gave rise to maggots, which then turned into flies (Miller and Levine, 1991, p. 339). Some scientists, however, began to challenge this idea.

Redi hypothesized that the maggots actually arose from tiny eggs that were laid by flies on the meat. The eggs, he claimed, were too small to be seen by the human eye. In 1688, he conducted experiments to test his hypothesis. Redi placed meat in jars, some of which were left open to the air, and some of which were covered with netting or were tightly sealed. Maggots were found to grow only on the meat that flies could reach. Thus, it was determined that life did not spontaneously generate on the rotted meat (Miller and Levine, 1991, p. 340).

Lazzaro Spallanzani (1729-1799)

An eighteenth century English scientist, John Needham, attacked the findings of Redi. He claimed that his own scientific experiments verified that microorganisms **did** in fact spontaneously generate in some gravy, after it was allegedly thoroughly boiled in a bottle. Thus, in 1768, Lazzaro Spallanzani conducted his own simple scientific experimentation to test Needham's findings. He prepared gravy in the same manner that Needham had, divided it into two bottles, and boiled it thoroughly, killing all microorganisms. One of the bottles was corked, and the other was left open to the air. Spallanzani argued that if microorganisms were spontaneously generating from the gravy, the gravy from both bottles should be teeming with microorganisms after a few days. However, only the gravy in the open bottle was found to have microorganisms after the allotted time. Once again, it was determined that life does not spontaneously generate. Life comes only from other life (Miller and Levine, 1991, pp. 339-340).

Louis Pasteur (1822-1895)

For many, the work of Spallanzani and Redi was still not enough to drive the proverbial nail into the coffin of spontaneous generation. Some argued that air was needed for the spontaneous generation of life to occur, and Spallanzani's corked bottle did not allow air to reach the gravy. A standard, evolution-based high school biology textbook states: "It was not until 1864, and the elegant experiment of French scientist Louis Pasteur, that the hypothesis of spontaneous generation was finally **disproved**" (Miller and Levine, 1991, p. 341, emp. added). Pasteur placed a "nutrient broth," similar to Needham's gravy, in a flask with a long, s-curved neck. The flask was unsealed—left open to the air. However, the curvature of the flask's neck served as an entrapment mechanism for dust particles and airborne microorganisms, keeping them from reaching the broth. The flask was observed over the time span of an entire year, and microorganisms could never be found. Next, he broke off the s-curved neck of the flask, allowing dust and microorganisms to reach the broth. After only one day, the broth was cloudy from dust and teeming with microorganisms. According to the aforementioned biology textbook, "Pasteur, like Redi and Spallanzani before him, had shown that **life comes only from life**" (Miller and Levine, 1991, p. 341, emp. added). Pasteur had scientifically refuted the only naturalistic theory that was available for the origin of life.

Rudolf Virchow (1821-1902)

German scientist, Rudolf Virchow, further expanded scientific understanding of the Law of Biogenesis. Virchow "recognized that all cells come from cells by binary fusion" ("Definition...," 2006). In 1858, he made the discovery for which he is well-known—"*omnis cellula e cellula*"—"every cell originates from another existing cell like

59

it" ("Definition..."). The *Encyclopaedia Britannica* says, concerning Virchow, "His aphorism *'omnis cellula e cellula'*... ranks with Pasteur's *'omne vivum e vivo'* ('every living thing [arises] from a [preexisting] living thing') **among the most revolutionary generalizations of biology**" (see "Rudolf Virchow," 1973, 23:35, emp. added, parenthetical items in orig.). So, in nature, life comes from life **of its own kind**.

In Search of an Evolutionary Explanation

In spite of the lack of evidence for abiogenesis and the decisive evidence against it, many scientists simply refuse to accept the evidence. This refusal to accept the impossibility of abiogenesis commonly results in many scientists and media personnel jumping to quick, rash conclusions about any new research which gives a glimmer of hope to the idea of abiogenesis. When a researcher's work can conceivably be twisted by the media to support the hope of spontaneous generation, it seems that many evolutionists will strive to do so—against all reason to the contrary.

Monera

In 1876, German scientist Ernst Haeckel claimed that he had found a life form so simple that it made abiogenesis seem more plausible. "Monera," as he called them, were

> organisms which are, in fact, not composed of any organs at all, but consist entirely of shapeless, simple, homogenous matter. The entire body of one of these Monera, during life, is nothing more than a shapeless, mobile, little lump of mucus or slime, consisting of an albuminous combination of carbon. Simpler or more imperfect organisms we cannot possibly conceive (Haeckel, 1876, 1:184).

In spite of his wild claims that his find had been established as fact by other famous scientists, the truth about Monera had already been

The Law of Biogenesis
vs. Evolution [Part I]

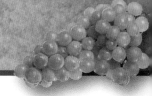

shown to be quite different before his findings were even published. Monera proved to be lifeless, inorganic compounds—amorphous gypsum that precipitated out of sea-water by alcohol (Grigg, 1996). The jump from non-life to life is simply no trivial matter, regardless of the assertions of rash scientists. [See Houts, 2011 for further discussion.]

Miller-Urey Experiment

In 1953, American scientists Stanley Miller and Harold Urey created the alleged planetary atmospheric conditions that would have been in existence billions of years ago when life supposedly originated on Earth. They did this by "mixing methane, ammonia, water, and hydrogen in a flask" (Miller and Levine, 1991, p. 343; Miller, 1953). They then passed "ultraviolet light electric sparks" through the mixture to simulate sunlight and lightning (1991, p. 343). What **were** the results of the experiment? Was life created? The product was a mixture composed primarily of what was essentially tar plus two simple amino acids, which are among the building blocks of proteins. The experiment came nowhere near creating life.

Further, the experiment was conducted without the presence of oxygen, since the presence of oxygen in the experiment would have quickly oxidized any amino acids that were formed and, in turn, would have prevented the formation of life. Miller and Levine, in their biology textbook, noted that, "All these experiments produced important organic molecules, including ATP and the nitrogenous base adenine, **in the absence of oxygen**" (1991, p. 344, emp. added). Evolutionary scientists now admit that, according to the evolutionary model, such would not have characterized Earth's atmosphere at that time. They believe Earth's atmosphere **would have** in fact contained oxygen in their hypothetical (i.e., mythical) model, thus preventing the origin of life in that way. NASA reported that a "reducing atmosphere," which was assumed by the Miller-Urey experiment, has never existed (Levine, 1983). What's more, they realize that the simulated atmospheric conditions of the Miller-Urey experiment would have made the synthesis of organic molecules virtually impossible and that ultraviolet radiation from sunlight is actually destructive—not beneficial—to life.

Evolutionist Robert Shapiro discussed the products of the Miller-Urey experimentation, saying:

> Let us sum up. The experiment performed by Miller yielded tar as its most abundant product. There are about fifty small organic compounds that are called "building blocks." Only two of these fifty occurred among the preferential Miller-Urey products (1986, p. 105).

In spite all of the "hullabaloo," the truth is that the Miller-Urey experiment not only did not create life, but it did not even create 5% of the building blocks necessary for life to exist. The evolutionists admit and even teach as much—albeit, as inconspicuously as possible. One junior high, evolution-based textbook, *Life Sciences*, concedes: "Although the Miller-Urey experiment showed that chemicals **found in** living things could be produced, it **did not prove** that life began in this way" (*National Geographic..., et al.*, 2005, p. 21, emp. added).

Robert Hazen, in his the lecture series *Origins of Life*, stated that since the Miller-Urey experiment, "almost every kind of biomolecule has been made, including most of life's amino acids, membrane-forming hydrocarbons, energy-rich sugars, and other carbohydrates and metabolic acids as well" (2005). However, the truth still remains: (1) scientists cannot create life in a laboratory, much less in a natural environment; (2) atheistic evolutionists have no evidence that life could spontaneously generate itself into existence, regardless of the environmental conditions and regardless of the presence of life's building blocks; and (3) even if there were environmental conditions which would allow for the spontaneous generation of life, evolutionists cannot state with scientific certainty that such conditions would have **ever** been in existence, much less at the precise time needed for the origin of life. That is precisely why Hazen conceded the following:

> I have to be honest, even with a scientific approach there is a possibility that we will never know—in fact, that we **cannot** ever know—how life emerged. That is because it is always possible that life emerged by an almost infinitely improbable sequence of difficult chemical reactions.... If that is true, then any scientific attempt to understand life's origins is doomed to failure (2005, emp. added).

Precisely. The Miller-Urey experiment did nothing but confuse the ultimate issue in the minds of millions of people. Atheistic evolution

The Law of Biogenesis
vs. Evolution [Part I]

cannot even get off the ground as a theory of life origins since it has no possible scientific way in which it can begin.

Another problem with the Miller-Urey experiment arises when considering the phenomenon known as chirality, which Louis Pasteur is credited with discovering in 1848 due to his work with sodium ammonium tartrate (Gal, 2011, p. 1). Pasteur found that some molecules contain dissymmetry—that is, they have no internal plane of symmetry. Similar to the idea that one's hands are mirror images of each another, certain organic molecules (i.e., chiral molecules) exhibit such behavior. Pasteur further discovered that living things are "single-handed" in their molecular make-up, instead of being comprised of a 50-50 mixture of both "hands." This feature he highlighted as a defining characteristic of life, and in so doing, dealt a further deathblow to the idea of abiogenesis. The statistical impossibility of arriving at a single-handed molecular make-up cannot be denied. The problem that chirality presents for the Miller-Urey experiment comes from the fact that amino acids exist in both left- and right-handed forms, but life uses only left-handed amino acid forms. Miller-Urey type experiments produce a mixture of both forms of amino acids, rather than only left-handed forms. Thus, Miller-Urey type mixtures are incapable of forming proteins—and incapable of forming life. [See Houts, 2007, p. 84 and Sarfati, 1998a, 12[3]:263-266 for more information on the problem of chirality.]

Thus, the experiment did not prove life could come from non-life. Rather, it once again proved just the opposite. Miller and Levine admitted, "Scientists now know that Miller and Urey's original simulations of Earth's early atmosphere were not accurate" (2006, p. 424). Have the results of the experiment been abandoned? Certainly not. They are still touted in evolution-based textbooks today—including Miller and Levine's (2006, p. 424)!

It appears that scientific evidence, when in contradiction with evolutionary theory, has not stopped evolutionists from twisting the results of the Miller-Urey experiments to support their evolutionary propaganda. Another life science textbook states: "This [i.e., the Miller-Urey experiment—JM] showed that [not living things, but—JM] substances **present in** living things *could* [not "do"—JM] come from nonliving materials in the environment. It **did not prove** that life was formed in this way.... [S]cientists are still investigating where the first life came from" (Daniel, Ortleb, and Biggs, 1999, p. 12, italics in orig., emp. added). And they will continue to do so indefinitely—until they accept the implications of the evidence. Bottom line: life comes from life, no matter how many scientists refuse to admit it.

"Spontaneous Organization"—Wong, et al.

In June of 2000, a team of scientists conducted experiments that once again resulted in evolutionists scrambling to claim that life had been artificially created. Wong and his colleagues reported an experimental method whereby chemicals would spontaneously organize themselves into ribbon-like tubules that resembled three-layered, bacterial cell walls, similar to the plasma membranes that surround most cells (288:2035). Though the impression left is that spontaneous generation has occurred, the researchers hardly created life. Instead, they simply mixed the structure-providing protein, actin, with special liposomes to make actin-membrane capsules. These capsules do not possess DNA, do not actively metabolize, and do not reproduce. Therefore, they contain none of the characteristics that scientists look for to identify life. Bottom line: spontaneous **organization** may occur—**not** spontaneous generation. [See Thompson and Harrub, 2003 for further discussion.]

Manmade Bone?—Hartgerink, et al.

In 2001, Jeffrey Hartgerink and his colleagues reported that they had made self-assembling synthetic bone (2001). This beneficial research was described by the media as the scientists having created "manmade bone." Such descriptions give a subtle impression that life has been created by humans. After all, bone is considered to be a living organ. A close analysis of the experiment, however, reveals that life was not created at all. A bone merely lying on a table cannot be construed as being alive, especially without blood—the life-sustaining agent—flowing through it.

Daddy Diamond?—Sommer, et al.

In 2008, German scientists conducted experiments on diamonds to test the theory that life could have started as a result of processes that took place on diamonds billions of years ago (Sommer, et al., 2008). The researchers explain:

> The circumstance that **water** [that is] adsorbed from the air [i.e., water accumulated on the surface—JM] becomes crystalline at room temperature attracted in fact more attention than the revelation of the implication of this water in the surface **conductivity** of hydrogenated diamond, a new feature in the 20-year-old puzzle. The report of our results triggered an intense discussion on the implications of water in the mechanism of surface conductivity on hydrogen-terminated diamond.... That life **could have** started with crystalline **water** layers inducing order to prebiotic molecules on solid surfaces was predicted by Albert Szent-Gyorgyi. Mineral surfaces are catalytic platforms, **regarded as necessary** during the emergence of life on Earth—because the assembly of complex bioorganic molecules by random collisions in an aqueous environment is implausible. Carbon **seems to** represent even better platforms (8[8]:2628, emp. added).

So, the researchers have determined that when water adsorbs (i.e., accumulates on the surface of a material) from the air onto diamonds, a crystalline structure forms on its surface, which affects the diamond's electrical conductivity. According to the researchers, "[T]he conductivity on natural diamond was better by a factor of 10 than that on synthetic diamond" (p. 2628).

Now, what is the implied point being made? Water plus crystalline structures plus electrical conductivity yields life. But wait! How can that be? These components are still around today, and life has not spontaneously originated from their mixture, no matter how many times a diamond ring is dipped in water and shocked. The truth is that the researchers, though discovering an interesting characteristic of diamonds, ultimately went **nowhere** in trying to shed light on the spontaneous origin of life. As was the case with all previously conducted scientific experimentation, the scientists did not create life through their experiments, and they did nothing to prove what the planetary conditions must have been like for abiogenesis to allegedly occur. No wonder the researchers begin their article by admitting:

> The emergence of bioorganic molecules under primitive Earth conditions is one of the major **unsolved origin of life questions**. The principal problem is to identify physical and chemical conditions that are favorable for the formation of life precursor structures (p. 2628, emp. added).

Scientists can only guess and speculate about the origin of life, which is precisely the basis of the researchers' work. The article is riddled with disclaimers—"could," "could have started," "possible," and "seems to." Although the authors certainly **proved nothing** about the origin of life or the planetary conditions that allegedly would have been in existence millions of years ago at life's inception, they made up for their lack of proof with abundant speculation.

What's more, the foundation of their origin of life research involves the assumption that, "[d]iamonds are older than the earliest forms of life on Earth" (p. 2629). If diamonds are not as old as they think, life could not have originated on their surfaces. Recent research conducted by the RATE (Radioisotopes and the Age of the Earth) research team casts serious doubt on this significant assumption (DeYoung, 2005). Further, even if they could determine planetary conditions that may be conducive to the formation of life, they still have the problem of explaining how that life could then come into existence from non-life in contradiction to the Law of Biogenesis (see Butt, 2008a for related discussion on the Sommer, Zhu, and Fecht research).

Life from a Bottle?—Gibson, et al.

In 2010, Gibson and his colleagues reported having created life from "four bottles of chemicals" (Sanders, 2010). In this study, a bacterial cell's chromosome was replaced with a "chemically synthesized genome" (Gibson, et al., 2010). Biochemist Joe Deweese discussed several considerations concerning this study:

> 1) the DNA sequences for all of the genes were **already designed** and synthesizers were used to generate the actual DNA; 2) the recipient cell contained preformed enzymes and other factors needed to support life—**the cell was not "made from scratch"**; 3) the sole replaced

component in the recipient cell was the "instructions," that is, the DNA; and 4) the researchers relied on **living** systems to help assemble the chromosome into its final form through the stitching process in yeast (Deweese, 2010, emp. in orig.).

Life was not made from non-life. We eagerly await the day when atheistic evolutionists stop rushing to conclusions and twisting the evidence and, instead, accept what science has already **proven** to be true. Sadly, our wait may be in vain. Regardless, as Sir Fred Hoyle and Chandra Wickramasinghe, professor of astronomy and applied mathematics at University College, Cardiff, Wales, said, "Be **suspicious** of a theory if **more and more hypotheses** are needed to support it as new facts become available, or as new considerations are brought to bear" (1981, p. 135, emp. added).

Recreating Molecules That Gave Birth to Life?— Burroughs, et al.

Perhaps from the above you are noticing a disturbing trend. It is often very easy to be misled by the media and the scientific community by how they report matters relating to the origin of life. The impression is sometimes left that scientists have finally discovered the origin of life, as though the case is closed. "Abiogenesis occurred, and here's how it happened."

In 2012, *Mail Online* ran an article boldly titled, "British Scientists Recreate the Molecules that Gave Birth to Life Itself" (Enoch, 2012). Such irresponsible titles send a false message to the public. The impression is left that, "It has finally been discovered how life spontaneously originated and the work of these scientists has proven it!" The team of scientists published their findings in the professional journal, *Organic and Biomolecular Chemistry* (Burroughs, et al., 2011). The scientists claimed to have achieved "the first step" on the "pathway to show how simple sugars [necessary for life—JM]...originated" (Enoch). But notice again, when one looks through the smoke from the technical jargon of the articles, he discovers that life was not created. Paul Clarke, who led the team of scientists, admitted, "For life to have evolved, you have to have a moment when non-living things become living—everything **up to that point** is chemistry. We are trying to understand the **chemical** origins of life" (Enoch, emp. added). So,

Clark acknowledged that his team's research does not even involve trying to answer the ultimate question of how life could come from non-life. His team was merely interested in trying to figure out how the non-living building blocks of life could come about—not how they could make the jump to life. That question is still untouched by Clark's team, and a mystery to the scientific world at large.

And further, the team made several grandiose assumptions concerning their sugar research. Their work applies to a **hypothetical** world that **allegedly might** have existed eons ago. That world **might** have had just the right conditions and **might** have had the available materials to produce the results **they** gathered from their experiments—conditions and materials which have only been present in their laboratory, not in nature. These results **may or may not** have been the means by which, in the evolutionist's eyes, life could have somehow spontaneously arrived in the first place. So ultimately, the research is meaningless when applied to the matter of origins. Speculation about a non-existent environment that would allow unscientific phenomena like abiogenesis to occur is like believing in the mythical world of Harry Potter (see Miller, 2012a for more on this research).

The Result: The Law of Biogenesis

So what has all of this scientific investigation proved? What can be drawn from the evidence? In nature, life comes only from life of its own kind. Period. All scientific evidence confirms this well-established principle of science. There are no known exceptions. Thus, biogenesis is a **law**. Abiogenesis is impossible. Prominent marine biologist and evolutionist Martin Moe admitted: "A century of sensational discoveries in the biological sciences has taught us that life arises **only** from life" (1981, p. 36, emp. added). George G. Simpson stated, "[T]here is no serious doubt that biogenesis is **the rule**, that life comes only from other life, that a cell, the unit of life, is **always** and **exclusively** the product or offspring of another cell" (Simpson and Beck, 1965, p. 144, emp. added). In their textbook, *Biology: A Search for Order in Complexity*, Moore and Slusher wrote: "Historically the point of view that **life comes only from life** has been so well established through the facts revealed by experiment that it is called the *Law* of Biogenesis" (1974, p. 74, emp. in orig., italics added). Neil Shubin,

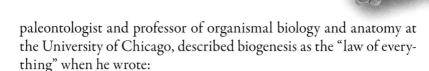

The Law of Biogenesis
vs. Evolution [Part I]

paleontologist and professor of organismal biology and anatomy at the University of Chicago, described biogenesis as the "law of everything" when he wrote:

> I can share with you one true law that all of us can agree upon. This law is so profound that most of us take it completely for granted. Yet it is the starting point for almost everything we do in paleontology, developmental biology, and genetics. This biological "law of everything" is that every living thing on the planet had parents. Every person you've ever known has biological parents, as does every bird, salamander, or shark you have ever seen.... To put it in a more precise form: every living thing sprang from some parental genetic information (2009, p. 174).

Life always comes from life. Children always come from parents. But naturalistic evolution requires abiogenesis—parentless children. That does not happen, according to the "one true law"—the "law of everything." Evolution simply does not harmonize with the evidence. It is unscientific.

What does the scientific evidence indicate about the origin of life? Life creates life. Naturalistic evolutionists themselves begrudgingly admit this, and yet refuse to accept its implications. If atheistic evolution is true, abiogenesis **must** be true, in spite of evidence to the contrary. Belief in abiogenesis is a stubborn refusal to accept the scientific evidence, choosing in turn to give credence to evolutionary superstition, myths, and fables.

Science vs. Evolution

Common Quibbles

- "Abiogenesis is Irrelevant to Evolution." [See Appendix 4.a]
- "Haven't Synthetic Biologists Created Life?" [See Appendix 4.b]

Review Questions

1) What four scientists are credited with establishing the validity of the Law of Biogenesis?
2) Have scientists created life from non-life in a laboratory?
3) What is abiogenesis?
4) What does the Law of Biogenesis say?
5) What famous experiments are still used as "evidence" for evolution in most biology textbooks today, even though they have been shown to be useless in proving abiogenesis?

Chapter 6

The Law of Biogenesis vs. Evolution [Part II]

Evolutionists' Candid Admissions Concerning Abiogenesis

"It's impossible"

In light of the extensive amount of scientific evidence against abiogenesis, many scientists have made candid admissions about it. Evolutionist and science writer John Horgan conceded that if he were a creationist, he would focus on the origin of life to prove his position, because it

> is by far the weakest strut of the chassis of modern biology. The origin of life is a science writer's dream. It abounds with exotic scientists and exotic theories, which are never entirely abandoned or accepted, but merely go in and out of fashion (1996, p. 138).

Hosts of high school, evolution-based biology textbooks commonly make comments concerning Pasteur's experiments like, "the hypothesis of spontaneous generation was finally **disproved**" (Miller and Levine, 1991, p. 341, emp. added). Yet they continue to propagate evolutionary dogma and the spontaneous generation of life, sometimes on the very next page of the book (Miller and Levine, 1991, p. 342). George Wald wrote: "As for spontaneous generation, it continued to find acceptance until finally **disposed of** by the work of Louis Pasteur" (1962, p. 187, emp. added). He further stated: "One has only to contemplate the magnitude of this task to concede that the spontaneous generation of a

living organism is **impossible**. Yet here we are, as a result, I believe, of spontaneous generation" (1954, p. 47, emp. added). So, "spontaneous generation is impossible, but I'm going to believe it anyway"?

Hoyle and Wickramasinghe discussed the origin of life, saying:

> Once we see, however, that the probability of life originating at random is so utterly minuscule as to make the random concept **absurd**, it becomes sensible to think that the favourable properties of physics on which life depends, are in every respect **deliberate**.... It is therefore almost inevitable that our own measure of intelligence must reflect in a valid way the higher intelligences...even to the extreme idealized limit of God (1981, pp. 141,144, emp. added).

Evolutionist J.D. Bernal, one of the leading scientists among x-ray crystallographers and the man who coined the term, "biopoesis" (Bernal, 1951), stated: "It is possible to demonstrate effectively...how life **could not have arisen**; the improbabilities are too great, the chances of the emergence of life too small. **Regrettably** from this point of view, life is here on earth...and **the arguments have to be bent around** to support its existence" (Bernal, 1967, p. 120, emp. added). In other words, "Life could not have spontaneously generated, but I refuse to accept the only alternative. The arguments must be bent to explain everything without the need of that alternative." Such a rationale (if it can be deemed **rational**e at all) is hardly scientific.

Not only do evolutionists recognize that arriving at life from non-life is impossible, but many even concede that the problem is far worse than that. They conjecture (rather wildly) about what the conditions on Earth must have been like to produce life. However, they realize that arriving at those conditions would have been equally as impossible as the actual jump from non-life to life. John Keosian, former biology professor at Rutgers University, said, "Even conceptually, it is difficult to see how a system satisfying the minimum criteria for a living thing can arise by chance and, **simultaneously, include a mechanism containing the suitable information for its own replication**" (Keosian, 1964, pp. 69-70, emp. added). Writing in *New Scientist*, Hoyle and Wickramasinghe lamented concerning the "prebiotic" soup allegedly necessary before abiogenesis could occur:

The Law of Biogenesis
vs. Evolution [Part II]

Precious little in the way of biochemical evolution could have happened on the Earth. **It is easy to show** that the two thousand or so enzymes that span the whole of life **could not have evolved** on Earth. If one counts the number of trial assemblies of amino acids that are needed to give rise to the enzymes, the probability of their discovery by random shufflings turns out to be less than 1 in $10^{40,000}$ (1991, 91:415, emp. added).

John Horgan wrote in *Scientific American*:

DNA cannot do its work, including forming more DNA, without the help of catalytic proteins, or enzymes. In short, proteins cannot form without DNA, but neither can DNA form without proteins. But as researchers continue to examine the RNA-world concept closely, **more problems** emerge. How did RNA arise initially? RNA and its components are difficult to synthesize in a laboratory under the best of conditions, **much less under plausible prebiotic ones** (1991, 264:119, emp. added).

A decade later, Horgan was still at a loss concerning the origin of DNA, RNA, and enzymes. Again writing for *Scientific American*, he wrote, "DNA can make neither proteins nor copies of itself without the help of catalytic proteins called enzymes. This fact turned the origin of life into a classic chicken-or-egg puzzle: Which came first, proteins or DNA?" (2011). That's quite a problem. How likely is it that DNA **and** its necessary proteins happened to evolve at exactly the same moment? Again, Horgan pressed the fact that the RNA-world hypothesis is not the answer. "The RNA world is so dissatisfying that some frustrated scientists are resorting to much more **far out**—literally—**speculation**" (2011, emp. added). In concluding his article, he stated: "Creationists are no doubt thrilled that origin-of-life research has reached such an impasse..." (2011). He is right about one thing. Creationists are thrilled at such findings. However, the thrill is not from origin-of-life research reaching an "impasse." Rather, it is from the removal of an impasse in front of scientists commencing **true** origin-of-life research.

Evolutionists themselves realize that abiogenesis is impossible. The *McGraw-Hill Dictionary of Scientific and Technical Terms* defines "abiogenesis" as, "**the obsolete concept** that plant and animal life arise from nonliving organic matter," although the contributors would hardly be deemed creationists (2003, p. 3, emp. added). It bears repeating: the notion of spontaneous generation is an **obsolete concept!**

"We Don't Have a Clue"

Given the impossibility of abiogenesis, one might logically ask the evolutionist, "If abiogenesis is impossible, and you won't accept God, how, then, did life arise?" Over eighty years ago, evolutionist John Sullivan admitted what remains true to this day:

> The beginning of the evolutionary process raises a question which is yet **unanswerable**. What was the origin of life on this planet? Until fairly recent times there was a pretty general belief in the occurrence of "spontaneous generation".... But careful experiments, notably those of Pasteur, showed that this conclusion was due to imperfect observation, and it became **an accepted doctrine that life never arises except from life**. So far as the **actual evidence** goes, this is still the **only** possible conclusion (1933, p. 94, emp. added).

The disciple of evolution might very well reply, "Well, that was over 80 years ago. We know how it all happened now." Moving into the 1960s, the question was still unanswered. Chemists D.E. Green and R.F. Goldberger asked:

> How, then, did the precursor cell arise? The only unequivocal rejoinder to this question is that **we do not know**.... There is one step [in evolution—JM] that far outweighs the others in enormity: the step from macromolecules to cells. All the other steps can be accounted for on theoretical grounds—if not **correctly**, at least elegantly. The macromolecule-to-cell transition is a jump of **fantastic dimensions**, which lies beyond the range of testable hypothesis. In this area **all is conjecture**. The available facts do not provide a basis for postulating that cells arose on this planet. This is not to say that some para-physical forces were not at work. We simply wish to point out that **there is no scientific evidence** (1967, p. 403,406-407, emp. added).

In the late 1970s, Jastrow said, regarding the evolution of life:

> According to this story, every tree, every blade of grass, and every creature in the sea and on the land evolved out of one parent strand of molecular matter drifting lazily in a warm pool. What concrete **evidence** supports that remarkable theory of the origin of life? **There**

is none.... At present, science has **no satisfactory answer** to the question of the origin of life on the earth (1977, p. 60, 62-63, emp. added).

One might suppose, "Surely, by the 1980s an answer had been reached!" Evolutionist Douglas Hofstadter said,

> There are various theories on the origin of life. They all run aground on this most central of all central questions: "How did the Genetic Code, along with the mechanisms for its translation (ribosomes and RNA molecules) originate?" For the moment, we will have to content ourselves with a sense of **wonder and awe rather than with an answer** (1980, p. 548, emp. added).

Evolutionist Andrew Scott, writing in *New Scientist*, observed:

> Take some matter, heat while stirring, and wait. That is the modern version of Genesis. The "fundamental" forces of gravity, electromagnetism and the strong and weak nuclear forces are presumed to have done the rest.... But how much of this neat tale is firmly established, and how much remains **hopeful speculation**? In truth, the mechanism of almost every major step, from chemical precursors up to the first recognizable cells, is the subject of either **controversy** or **complete bewilderment**.
>
> We are grappling with a classic "chicken and egg" dilemma. Nucleic acids are required to make proteins, whereas proteins are needed to make nucleic acids and also to allow them to direct the process of protein manufacture itself.
>
> The emergence of the gene-protein link, an absolutely vital stage on the way up from lifeless atoms to ourselves, is still shrouded in almost **complete mystery**.... We still know **very little** about how our genesis came about, and to provide a more satisfactory account than we have at present **remains** one of science's **great challenges** (1985, 106:30-33, emp. added).

Klaus Dose of the Institute for Biochemistry at Johannes Gutenberg University, pointed out:

> More than 30 years of experimentation on the origin of life in the fields of chemical and molecular evolution have led to a better perception of the **immensity of the problem** of the origin of life on Earth rather than to its solution. At present all discussions on principal theories and experiments in the field either end in stalemate or in a confession of **ignorance** (1988, 13[4]:348, emp. added).

The arrival of the 1990s in no way assisted evolutionists in finding an answer for the origin of life. Evolutionist John Maddox, writing in *Nature*, said, "[I]t is disappointing that the origin of the genetic code is **still as obscure** as the origin of life itself" (1994, 367:111, emp. added). And today, scientists are **still** at a loss as to how life could have arisen spontaneously. In the lecture series *Origins of Life*, Robert Hazen made several notable admissions:

- "This course is unusual because at this point in time, there is **so much that we don't know** about life on Earth."
- "The origin of life is a subject of immense complexity, and I have to tell you right up front, **we don't know how life began**."
- "It's as if we are trying to assemble a huge jigsaw puzzle. We have a few pieces clumped together here and there, but **most of the puzzle pieces are missing**."
- "How can I tell you about the origin of life when we are **so woefully ignorant** of that history?"

Incredibly, he further conceded:

> This course focuses exclusively on the scientific approach to the question of life's origins. In this lecture series, I make an **assumption** that life emerged from basic raw materials through a sequence of events that was completely consistent with the natural laws of chemistry and physics. Even with this scientific approach, there is a possibility that we'll never know—in fact, that **we can't ever know**. It is possible that life emerged by an almost infinitely improbable sequence of difficult chemical reactions. If life is the result of an infinitely improbable succession of chemical steps, then any scientific attempt to understand life's origin is **doomed to failure**; such a succession **could not be duplicated** in a program of lab experiments. If the origin of life was an infinitely improbable accident, then there's absolutely **nothing** you or I or anyone else could do to figure out how it happened. I must tell you, that's a depressing thought to someone like me who has devoted a decade to understanding the origin of life (2005, emp. added).

Paul Davies, writing in *New Scientist*, said, "One of the great outstanding scientific mysteries is the origin of life. How did it happen?... The truth is, **nobody has a clue**" (2006, 192[2578]:35, emp. added). Richard Dawkins stated in an interview with Ben Stein regarding

the origin of life, "**Nobody knows** how it got started. We know the kind of event that it must have been. We know the sort of event that must have happened for the origin of life. It was the origin of the first self-replicating molecule." Stein asked, "Right. And how did that happen?" Dawkins replied, "I've told you. We don't know." Stein then said, "So, you have no idea how it started?" Dawkins replied, "No. **Nor has anybody**" (Stein and Miller, 2008, emp. added). John Horgan did not even try to hide his admission **within** an article. He titled one of his articles, "Pssst! Don't Tell the Creationists, but Scientists **Don't Have a Clue How Life Began**" (2011, emp. added). Such admissions are quite telling, albeit incorrect. What Davies, Horgan, Dawkins, and all of the other scientists that have been quoted thus far mean is, no **naturalist** "has a clue." Biblical **super**-naturalists, on the other hand, know **exactly** how life originated, and the answer harmonizes perfectly with the Law of Biogenesis—unlike evolution's life-origins fairytale. [NOTE: Since naturalism has thoroughly permeated the scientific community, naturalistic scientists are notorious for equating "science" with their naturalistic view and its theories, as though all scientists who do not believe in naturalism do not engage in real science and are not real scientists. Throughout this book, note the naturalists' synonomous use of the terms "science" and "naturalism/evolution" in their quotes, as though they are one and the same. Such a practice casts science in a bad light in general, since naturalism is self-contradictory and requires blind faith in several of its tenets (see Appendix 6.c and 6.e). Note, however, that the Creation model does not contradict the scientific evidence, and many scientists are creationists.]

"It's a miracle!"

So, according to atheistic evolutionists, the origin of life through spontaneous generation—a fundamental plank of evolutionary theory—is **impossible**. "Nobody has a clue" how life could have started. What conclusion is left for the naturalist? **It must have been a miracle**. No wonder many evolutionists, ironically, cautiously use religious terminology to describe the origin of life, in spite of the attacks they have made against the religiously minded community for doing so. Jastrow stated:

Science vs. Evolution

At present, science has no satisfactory answer to the question of the origin of life on the earth. Perhaps the appearance of life on the earth is a **miracle**. Scientists [i.e., naturalistic scientists—JM] are reluctant to accept that view, but their choices are limited; either life was created on the earth by the will of a being outside the grasp of scientific understanding, or it evolved on our planet spontaneously, through chemical reactions occurring in nonliving matter lying on the surface of the planet. The first theory places the question of the origin of life beyond the reach of scientific inquiry. It is a statement of faith in the power of a Supreme Being not subject to the laws of science. The second theory is also **an act of faith**. The act of faith consists in **assuming** that the scientific view of the origin of life is correct, **without having concrete evidence to support that belief** (1977, pp. 62-63, emp. added).

"Faith"? "Miracle"? Jastrow actually misuses the term "faith" in his description of creationists by implying our belief is one that is without "concrete evidence to support that belief" (and erroneously uses the term "science" synonomously with "naturalistic evolution"), but it is an amazing concession that Jastrow admits the naturalistic theory of life origins is a purely blind faith (see Appendix 6.e). Years ago, Sullivan admitted, "The hypothesis that life has developed from inorganic matter is, at present, still an **article of faith**" (p. 95, emp. added). Sir Francis Crick, co-discoverer of the double helix structure of the DNA molecule, conceded, "An **honest** man, armed with all the knowledge available to us now, could only state that in some sense, the origin of life appears at the moment to be almost a **miracle**, so many are the conditions which would have had to have been satisfied to get it going" (1981, p. 88, emp. added). G.A. Kerkut said that spontaneous generation is "**a matter of faith** on the part of the biologist.... The evidence for what did happen is **not available**" (1960, p. 150, emp. added).

The very people who claim that Bible believers are beholden to "ancient mythology" and "fables" without evidence are beginning to admit that **they**, in fact, are the ones guilty as charged. In his classic text, *The Immense Journey*, the late evolutionary anthropologist Loren Eiseley said the following regarding the idea of spontaneous generation:

With the failure of these many efforts, science was left in the somewhat embarrassing position of having to postulate theories of living origins which it could not demonstrate. After having chided the theologian for his reliance on myth and **miracle**, science found itself in the unenviable position of having to create a mythology of its own: namely, the **assumption** that what, after long effort, could not be proved to take place today, had, in truth, taken place in the primeval past (1957, pp. 201-202, emp. added).

Hoyle and Wickramasinghe concluded:

It is doubtful that anything like the conditions which were simulated in the laboratory existed at all on a primitive Earth, or occurred for long enough times and over sufficiently extended regions of the Earth's surface to produce large enough local concentrations of the biochemicals required for the start of life. In accepting the "primeval soup theory" of the origin of life, scientists have replaced **religious mysteries** which shrouded this question with **equally mysterious scientific dogmas**. The implied scientific dogmas are **just as inaccessible** to the empirical approach (1978, p. 26, emp. added).

If the origin of life is "a matter of faith" in the sense that no human being was physically present to observe it, then how can we determine which view—spontaneous generation or special creation—is the truth? The atheistic evolutionist insists: "I don't know how it happened, but I won't accept God." Such a mentality is hardly a willingness to honestly follow the evidence wherever it might lead. The Bible, however, asserts that the evidence is available for us to arrive at truth, and it is the truth that will set us free (John 8:32). It is not a "leap into the dark" without evidence. God "did not leave Himself without witness" (Acts 14:17). Knowledge of God's existence, and thus special creation, is not only attainable, but it is so readily available that those who reject the evidence are said to be "without excuse" (Romans 1:20). The created order "declares" the truth of the matter (Psalm 19:1).

Is it not true that the **reasonable** view on the origin of life will be the view that is in keeping with the evidence we **do** have? Why would science lie? It has no agenda or bias. Science should support the correct view—not contradict it. What does the evidence say? **In nature, life comes only from life and that of its kind. Therefore, abiogenesis**

does not happen. Science has proven this truth time and time again. To continue to champion abiogenesis is to hold to a view that flies in the face of the scientific evidence, taking a leap into the dark without proof. The only plausible option—an option that does not contradict the scientific evidence—is supernatural creation.

Self-delusion: A Powerful Force

"Well, I know it's impossible, but maybe..."

How do atheistic evolutionists get away with teaching a viewpoint that so brazenly contradicts the scientific evidence? Concerning this question, Wald said:

> Most...biologists, having reviewed with satisfaction the downfall of the spontaneous generation hypothesis, yet unwilling to accept the alternative belief in special creation, are left with nothing. [Actually, they "are left" with God.—JM] I think a scientist [read that, atheistic evolutionist—JM] has no choice but to approach the origin of life through a hypothesis of spontaneous generation. What the controversy reviewed above showed to be untenable is only the belief that living organisms arise spontaneously under **present conditions**. We have now to face a somewhat different problem: how organisms **may have** arisen spontaneously under **different conditions** in some former period, **granted** that they do so no longer (1954, pp. 46-47, cmp. added).

So, prebiotic planetary conditions were different? Conditions which would allow for the spontaneous generation of life? What is this conjecture based on? Has any evidence been brought to light which proves that there are **any possible conditions** that could lead to abiogenesis? No. Else scientists would be able to create life in a laboratory. Conclusion: "different conditions" = evidence-less speculation. "Abiogenesis is impossible, but life is here and had to come from somewhere. We, the atheistic evolutionary community, refuse to consider the God option. That leaves us with the **assumption** that Earth's planetary conditions must have allowed for the miracle of abiogenesis in the past. There is no evidence for such speculation, but who cares?" In his next breath, Wald went on to admit:

To make an organism demands the right substances in the right proportions and in the right arrangement. We do not **think** that anything more is needed—but that is problem enough. One has only to contemplate the magnitude of this task to concede that **the spontaneous generation of a living organism is impossible. Yet here we are**.... (1954, pp. 46-47, emp. added).

Evolutionists write, in essence, children's fables—full of wild speculation, theories, and conjecture about the **possible** pre-life planetary conditions, but ultimately their viewpoint is "inaccessible to the empirical approach" (Hoyle and Wickramasinghe, 1978, p. 26). Evolutionary biochemist Richard Dickerson of UCLA's Institute of Geophysics and Planetary Physics agreed with Wald. Writing in *Scientific American* under the heading of "Chemical Evolution and the Origin of Life," he remarked that when speculating about Earth's pre-biotic conditions we have "no laboratory models: hence one can **speculate** endlessly **unfettered by inconvenient facts**" (1978, p. 85, emp. added). He went on to concede: "We can only **imagine** what **probably** existed, and our imagination so far has **not** been very helpful" (p. 86, emp. added). So, basing theories upon imagination is now considered scientific.

Notice from this discussion that in holding to such a position about "pre-biotic conditions" atheistic evolutionists have nonchalantly moved away from the standard evolutionary model—recognizing that it simply cannot account for the existence of life. Evolutionary theory has historically been based on uniformitarian principles, which assume that geological processes existing today on Earth have existed throughout the past as well ("Uniformitarianism," 2012; "Uniformitarianism," 2003, p. 2224). Theorizing conditions that are not in existence today is, in effect, a rejection of standard evolutionary assumptions. It is the Creation model—not the evolutionary model—which has historically rejected uniformitarianism. Sadly, in today's scientific community, it appears that evolutionists have been given the freedom to cherry-pick what their standard assumptions will and will not apply to. How can such be deemed unbiased and scientific?

Science vs. Evolution

"Watch us convert young minds to the Church of Evolution, in spite of the evidence!"

Some 50 years ago, in *Frontiers of Modern Biology*, George Wald admitted:

> As for spontaneous generation, it continued to find acceptance until finally **disposed of** by the work of Louis Pasteur—it is a curious thing that until quite recently professors of biology habitually told this story as part of their introductions of students to biology. They would finish this account glowing with the conviction that they had given a telling demonstration of the overthrow of mystical notion by clean, scientific experimentation. Their students were usually so bemused as to forget to ask the professor how he accounted for the origin of life. This would have been an embarrassing question, because there are only two possibilities: either life arose by spontaneous generation, which the professor had just refuted; or it arose by supernatural creation, which he probably regarded as anti-scientific (1962, p. 187, emp. added).

According to Wald, in 1962 the **demise** of spontaneous generation was openly taught in biology classes "until quite recently," and then, with the next breath, the teacher would proceed to engage in self-contradiction by teaching evolutionary theory with its abiogenesis myth. Though this statement was made years ago, the same is still the case a half-century later. Consider the following evidence.

According to evolutionists, the planetary conditions must have been different in the distant past—more conducive to abiogenesis. Enter the endless speculation about the pre-biotic world. Consider an example of how such speculation plays out in the high school biology classroom. In one high school biology textbook from the 1990s, published by the popular company, *Prentice Hall*, immediately after explaining how Pasteur, Redi, and Spallanzani disproved spontaneous generation, the authors queried: "If life can come only from life, how did life on Earth first arise?" (Miller and Levine, 1991, p. 342). The student eagerly awaits the answer to this crucial question.

The book proceeds to speculate with bold certainty what conditions were like on Earth billions of years ago. The observant student, who is able to see through all of the jargon, will notice that throughout the ensuing discussion about these hypothetical conditions, subtle

82

The Law of Biogenesis
vs. Evolution [Part II]

disclaimers are made. "**No one** can say with **certainty**..."; "**Somehow** these earliest life forms appeared..." (p. 343, emp. added). While discussing the experiments of Miller and Urey conducted in 1953, the textbook says, "Thus, over the course of millions of years, at least **some** of the basic building blocks of life **could have** been produced in great quantities on Earth" (p. 344, emp. added). The authors proceed to admit concerning the experiment's products: "A collection of organic molecules such as amino acids is **certainly not life**" (p. 344, emp. added). So, no answer to the question yet—"If life can come only from life, how did life on Earth first arise?"

Next, as if emphasizing the power of intelligent design, the authors briefly discuss the experiments of Russian scientist Alexander Oparin and American scientist Sidney Fox and the round droplets (deemed "protolife") **they "created"** in their lab, which can "perform tasks necessary for life" (p. 344). However, they admit that, "we would **still not say** that these droplets are **alive**" (p. 344, emp. added). So, recapping the evolutionary rhetoric to this point: evolutionary theory's explanation of the origin of life is based on words and phrases such as, "no one can say with certainty," "somehow," "some," "could have," "certainly not life," and "still not say that these droplets are alive." The only solid, unqualified science discussed is that of Pasteur, Redi, and Spallanzani, who disproved abiogenesis, and by implication, naturalistic evolution. Recall further that the original point of the authors' discussion was to explain how life could have spontaneously arisen in the past, contrary to the work of Pasteur, Redi, and Spallanzani which they, themselves, reported. The authors, in spite of several paragraphs of "explanation," have yet to answer the question. Assuming they have a brilliant answer coming in the following paragraphs, the **ambitious** student reads on.

But unfortunately, by now, the authors have likely "lost" the **typical** student. At this point, these students, probably not catching the authors' disclaimers, will tend to "zone out" and just take the evolutionists' word for it—"So, we came from goo. Please move on." However, now the authors actually start to make candid, significant admissions. Under the heading "From Proto-life to Cells," the authors concede:

The next step in our story is **the most difficult to understand** completely. From the jumbled mixture of molecules in the organic soup that formed in Earth's oceans, the highly organized structures of RNA and DNA must **somehow** have evolved. Scientists **do not know how** these vital information-carriers formed, but there are several interesting **hypotheses** (pp. 344-345, emp. added).

No answers based on solid evidence that refute the Law of Biogenesis are established; instead, more baseless hypotheses. The authors proceed to give several imaginative suggestions for how matter could have arranged itself in preparation for life to spring into existence, liberally sprinkling in words like "could have arisen" and "might have combined." They finish off the section stating, "This is one piece of evidence supporting this interesting, but as yet **unproven, hypothesis**" (p. 345, emp. added). Notice that the authors still have yet to prove, or even less, attempt to explain, how spontaneous generation could have occurred. They spent their time presenting imaginary ways matter **could have** randomly and accidentally arranged itself in ways that **might** prepare it for life—although they have no way of knowing whether that arrangement would actually help or hinder the process, since abiogenesis has never been observed to occur, and since, to all intents and purpose, has already been shown to be scientifically unfeasible. No evidence was given for how matter could have actually sprung to life.

Finally, the authors simply **skip over** the ultimate question of how the spontaneous jump from inorganic matter to living cells occurred, perhaps correctly realizing that most of the dazed and confused students will not catch this subtle sleight of hand. The authors boldly state, "Although the origin of the first true cells is uncertain, we **can** identify several of their characteristics with **certainty**" (p. 345, emp. added). So, the student is quickly distracted and led away from the original question. According to the authors, scientists do not know how living cells actually spontaneously generated, but they assert they know "with certainty" what those cells were like once they mysteriously sprang into life. The authors state this assertion as if (1) they have decisively answered the original question about how life arose, and as if they were there, billions of years ago, to witness the process;

and (2) they could possibly know what the alleged protocells would have been like, even if they **could** spontaneously create themselves. They then proceed to speculate concerning the nature of these living cells, never answering the question of how they originally came to life. In all fairness, how could they answer such a question? Spontaneous generation has already been **disproven**—scientifically—and they admitted as much on previous pages. Yet they have conveniently failed to come to grips with the import of their own admissions.

The 2006 edition of the textbook did not rectify the problem. The authors acknowledge the work of Spallanzani and Pasteur, unabashedly stating that Pasteur's work

> convinced other scientists that the hypothesis of spontaneous generation **was not correct**. In other words, Pasteur showed that **all living things come from other living things**. This change in thinking represented a major shift in the way scientists viewed living things (Miller and Levine, 2006, pp. 12-13, emp. added).

Sadly the evolutionary community has not allowed Pasteur's findings to "shift" the way **they** view living things and their origins.

In this more recent edition, the authors "wisely" separated the discussion of Pasteur's and Spallazani's work from the discussion on the origin of life by 415 pages. This helps students to forget that naturalistic evolution contradicts the scientific evidence found by these scientists' work. In discussing the origin of life, the authors once again fail to accept the implied conclusion from Pasteur's work regarding the origin of life, stating, "As you will see shortly, researchers **still** debate such important questions as precisely how new species arise and why species become extinct. **There is also uncertainty about how life began**" (p. 386, emp. added).

The authors, undaunted, proceed to engage in the same hapless speculation they engaged in 15 years earlier. Similar to the previous edition, they discuss the findings, or rather non-findings, of the Miller-Urey experiments. A significant change in the 2006 edition was a candid admission about those experiments which was couched in the midst of the discussion. "Scientists now know that Miller and Urey's original simulations of Earth's early atmosphere **were not**

accurate" (p. 424, emp. added). If such is the case, one might rightly ask why the experiments are still discussed at all. The answer lies in the embarrassing fact that evolutionists still have absolutely no evidence that can corroborate abiogenesis. Leaving the discussion out would highlight the unscientific nature of naturalistic evolution. Leaving the discussion in the textbook leaves the impression with youth that there is still some hidden support of the abiogenesis postulate in the Miller-Urey experiments that is somehow too advanced to discuss with them at this point. After all, many youth are more likely to believe the teachers and textbooks they have been trained and taught to believe than they are to think critically about the material actually being presented.

In the next section, under the heading, "The Puzzle of Life's Origins," the authors admit, "A stew of organic molecules is a long way from a living cell, and **the leap from nonlife to life is the greatest gap in scientific hypotheses of Earth's early history**" (p. 425, emp. added). And that's it. Proof for abiogenesis is not presented. A scientific refutation of the Law of Biogenesis is not conducted. Once again, the authors fearlessly launch into pages of speculation concerning the origin of the building blocks of life, liberally using qualifying language to subtly admit that nothing the authors are saying has been proven. Concerning proteinoid microspheres, which have some cell-like characteristics but which are not considered living entities, the authors note, "Microspheres **are not cells**, but they have some characteristics of living systems.... Several **hypotheses** suggest that structures **similar** to proteinoid microspheres **might have** acquired more and more characteristics of living cells" (p. 425, emp. added). Such unending speculation, not backed by any proof whatsoever, is being allowed to fill the minds of unsuspecting youth, causing them to lose faith in the biblical model of life origins—which, in reality, is the origin model **actually in keeping with the scientific evidence**.

The authors proceed to admit once again, "Another **unanswered question** in the evolution of cells is the origin of DNA and RNA" (p. 425, emp. added). So, in their pointless trek to prove evolutionary theory, evolutionists cannot even **reach** the abiogenesis chasm

The Law of Biogenesis
vs. Evolution [Part II]

of impossibility that they must cross in order to prove their theory. They are still hampered by the chasms that exist much earlier in their mythical journey—the origin of DNA and RNA.

Notice that the phrase "unanswered question" can be misleading to a young biology student. It subtly leaves the impression that scientists **have** answered many questions about how life arose, and those answers are established fact. In actuality, the "unanswered question" is not referring to the question of whether or not evolutionists **know anything** about how life or its building blocks arose on the planet. The question is referring to the fact that there are questions regarding the **feasibility** of the origin of life that evolutionists cannot answer, but which must be answered in order for the theory of evolution even to be a possibility, much less the **true, factual scientific explanation** of the origin of life. Still, many unashamedly—and unscientifically—tout evolution as a fact.

In spite of the truth, sadly, with the wave of a hand, the typical biology student becomes an evolutionary disciple, not realizing that he has just succumbed to the longest, evidence-less leap into the dark that he may ever make in his life. Such vague speculation, substance-less hope, and blind "faith" can hardly be dignified as scientific. One might rightly ask, "Why are Americans allowing their children to be subjected to such anti-scientific propaganda? Why are parents not outraged that their students are wasting valuable class time learning about such speculative witchcraft, rather than learning true science?"

Science vs. Evolution

Common Quibble

- "Couldn't Life Have Come from Outer Space?" [See Appendix 4.c]

Review Questions

1) What are some of the candid admissions that evolutionists have made concerning the spontaneous generation of life?
2) What evidence indicates that belief in evolution is comparable to some religions?
3) What do many evolutionists assume about Earth's pre-biotic conditions?

Chapter 7

The Law of Biogenesis vs. Evolution [Part III]

Other Implications of the Law of Biogenesis

An Unreasonable Assumption which Leads to Contradiction of the Evidence

There is no scientific evidence in nature that life can come from non-life. Not one experiment has been conducted which can boast an exception to this rule. In order to even consider abiogenesis, one must start with the **assumption** that there is no Creator and that only the natural realm exists—in spite of all the evidence to the contrary. In his lecture series, *Origins of Life*, Robert Hazen said:

> In this lecture series I make a basic **assumption** that life emerged by some kind of natural process. I propose that life arose by a sequence of events that are completely consistent with the natural laws of chemistry and physics. **In this assumption I am like most other scientists.** I believe in a universe that is ordered by these natural laws. Like other scientists, I rely on the power of observations and experiments and theoretical reasoning to understand how the cosmos came to be the way it is (2005, emp. added).

[NOTE: Notice that Hazen contradicts himself by claiming that he relies "on the power of observations and experiments" in his belief about the origin of life. He admits in his lecture series that he and all evolutionists are "woefully ignorant" concerning the origin of life, and that potentially, "any scientific attempt to understand life's origin is **doomed to failure**; such a succession **could not be duplicated** in a

program of lab experiments" (2005, emp. added). He claims, however, to rely on "observations," "experiments," and "reasoning" to arrive at his scientific conclusions—one of which is abiogenesis. So, he accepts this belief without reason since it is not, and cannot be, backed by observation or experiment, and according to his own words, such may not ever even be possible.] Hazen states that he considers himself to be in line with "most other scientists" in his self-contradictory assumption regarding the naturalistic origin of life. Of course, he means "atheistic evolutionists" when he speaks of such "scientists" and is absolutely correct in his assertion.

Atheistic evolutionists begin with the biased assumption that there is no God, regardless of its contradictory and unsubstantiated nature. Atheistic evolutionist, prominent science writer, and director of the Knight Science Journalism Fellowship at M.I.T., Boyce Rensberger, admitted:

> At this point, it is necessary to reveal a little inside information about how scientists work, something the textbooks don't usually tell you. The fact is that scientists are not really as **objective and dispassionate in their work as they would like you to think**. Most scientists first get their ideas about how the world works not through rigorously logical processes but through hunches and **wild guesses**. As individuals they often come to believe something to be true long before they assemble the hard evidence that will convince somebody else that it is. Motivated by **faith** in his own ideas and a desire for **acceptance by his peers**, a scientist will labor for years knowing in his heart that his theory is correct but devising experiment after experiment whose results he hopes will support his position (1986, pp. 17-18, emp. added).

Rensberger's overgeneralized statement certainly does not describe all scientists' approach to their day-to-day research, but it is clear from its handling of the matter of origins that such a statement certainly describes the evolutionary mindset—hardly "objective and dispassionate," and often given to "wild guesses." Regardless, with the assumption in place that only the physical or natural exists—no Creator exists—abiogenesis **must** be true, since life is here and had to start somehow. Thus, if abiogenesis is true, biogenesis cannot be a law. [NOTE: Rather than making assumptions that do not contradict

the scientific evidence, evolutionists resort to unscientific assumptions—assumptions that contradict scientific laws which have been time-tested to be scientifically accurate 100% of the time.]

Consequently, some scientists have become increasingly uncomfortable with calling biogenesis a "law," since a scientific law, by definition, is "a regularity which applies to **all** members of a broad class of phenomena," and abio-

> ## Scientific Law:
> "A regularity which applies to all members of a broad class of phenomena."

genesis would constitute an exception, thus removing it from "law" status (*McGraw-Hill...*, 2003, p. 1182, emp. added). What once was commonly taught in textbooks due to its universal support by the scientific evidence is being systematically stripped from biology courses in spite of its **continued** universal support. In the commonly used middle school/junior high textbook, *Life Science*, the text's authors do not even mention the word "biogenesis," much less, "The Law of Biogenesis." Instead, under the heading, "Life Comes From Life," the authors explain the work of Redi and Pasteur and proudly proclaim:

> Living things arise from living things through reproduction.... The **mistaken** idea that living things can arise from nonliving sources is called spontaneous generation. It took hundreds of years of experiments to convince people that **spontaneous generation does not occur** (Coolidge-Stolz, et al., 2005, pp. 36-37, emp. added).

So, the truth of biogenesis still stands as law, though now stripped of its appropriate scientific designation. "Living things arise from living things"; "[S]pontaneous generation does not occur." Unfortunately, it seems that evolutionists, like these very authors, still have not gotten the memo. One would think that the admission, "spontaneous generation does not occur"—clearly implying there are no exceptions to this rule—would mean that biogenesis is still a law. After all, the same statements were made when it was still being publicly designated as a law. The only change appears to be the removal of the word "law," while still teaching the same truth. Starting on page 170, the authors proceed to teach evolutionary theory, never even addressing the question of how life could have come about—a question which must be

answered before the impossible theory of evolution could even begin its "work" billions of years ago.

Other textbooks still use the term "biogenesis," but have demoted its standing from that of a law. Under the heading, "Spontaneous Generation and Biogenesis," another prominent life science textbook briefly explains the work of Pasteur, stating that he "provided enough evidence to disprove the theory of spontaneous generation. It was replaced with biogenesis, which is the **theory** that living things come only from other living things" (*National Geographic...*, et al., 2005, p. 19, emp. added). Notice the sly adjustment from a "law" to a "theory." Why change biogenesis to a "theory" instead of a "law," particularly since the **same textbook** defines a "scientific law" as "a statement about how things work in nature that seems to be true all the time" (p. 10)—a statement which perfectly describes biogenesis? Based on this definition, has scientific investigation over the last several years nullified biogenesis as being a "law"? As we have already seen in previous chapters, the answer to that question is a resounding, "No." There is absolutely no evidence for abiogenesis. Thus, biogenesis, by all rights, is still a law, not a theory. Only the biased evolutionist will proclaim otherwise.

Again, in spite of "hundreds of years of experiments" (Coolidge-Stolz, et al., p. 37), in an attempt to lessen the certainty and implication of biogenesis, others are now calling it a "principle," instead of a law. Has experimentation proven there are exceptions to the validity of biogenesis? No. Quite the contrary is true. However, if it is considered to be a law, then atheistic evolution **cannot** be true, and one must then concede the existence of God. In their textbook, *Biology: A Search for Order in Complexity*, Moore and Slusher discussed the Law of Biogenesis. In a footnote, they say:

> Some philosophers call this a **principle** instead of a law, but this is a matter of definition, and definitions are arbitrary. Some scientists call this a **superlaw**, or a law about laws. Regardless of terminology, biogenesis has the highest rank in these levels of generalization (1974, p. 74, emp. in orig.).

In truth, calling Biogenesis a "principle" instead of a "law" does absolutely nothing to aid the evolutionary model, other than making its proponents falsely feel more comfortable with the self-contradictory viewpoint they embrace. After all, the *McGraw-Hill Dictionary of Scientific and Technical Terms* defines a "principle" as "**a scientific law** which is highly general or **fundamental**, and from which other laws are derived"

> ## Scientific Principle:
> "A scientific law which is highly general or fundamental, and from which other laws are derived."

(2003, p. 1671, emp. added). Evolutionists simply cannot escape the truth of the Law of Biogenesis. Evolution cannot be true, and the Law of Biogenesis also be true. Why go against the scientific evidence in support of an unscientific whim?

Humans...from Non-Humans?

There is another significant implication of the Law of Biogenesis, which was formally arrived at by Virchow. Even if a miraculous occurrence of abiogenesis were granted, another chasm still remains for the evolutionist to cross in order for his theory to be true. Perhaps you have seen the standard pictures illustrating the gradual evolution of man from ape-like creatures, like the one in the header at the top of this page? Evolutionists draw such pictures and proudly pronounce such ideas to be plausible and even factual. The result: Millions of disciples are made. However, the Law of Biogenesis stands in the way of this assertion as well.

Recall that the Law of Biogenesis says that life comes only from life, **and that of its kind**. This is what is meant by Virchow's discovery that "every cell originates from another existing cell **like it**" ("Definition...," 2006, emp. added). Similarly, in the words of the *McGraw-Hill Dictionary of Scientific and Technical Terms*, "biogenesis" is the "development of a living organism from a **similar living organism**" (2003, p. 239, emp. added). In the words of Stephen Meyer, whose doctoral dissertation at Cambridge University was in origin-of-life biology, "From ancient times, humans have known a few basic facts about

living things. The first is that all life comes from life. *Omne vivum ex vivo.* **The second is that when living things reproduce themselves, the resulting offspring resemble their parents. Like produces like**" (2009, Ch. 3, italics in orig., emp. added). For the same reason that dog-like creatures do not give birth to cats, horse-like creatures do not produce pigs, and frog-like creatures do not have snakes, it is also true that ape-like creatures do not give rise to humans. However, if evolutionary theory is true, this is, in essence, what happened.

In the field of philosophy, there is a law known as the Law of Excluded Middle, which says that every precisely stated proposition is either true or false (Jevons, 1888, p. 119). As long as one precisely states a proposition, it can be known to be either true or false. If we define a bald person as one having fewer than 200 hairs on his head, then every person is either bald or not bald. Similarly, as long as we precisely define what a human being is (and scientists **have** done so), every creature either is or is not human. In order for evolution to be true, the evolutionist must argue that a non-human has, in fact, given rise to a human at some point in the past—either by birth or by transformation (i.e., a non-human suddenly transformed into a human while alive). A proponent of transformation would likely be scoffed at, and the birth of a human from a non-human would violate the Law of Biogenesis. So, again, evolutionary theory is left with a gaping chasm that it cannot cross in hopes of attaining validity.

In the timeless, debate on the existence of God in 1976, philosopher and creationist Thomas Warren asked renowned, atheistic, evolutionary philosopher Antony Flew, of the University of Reading in England, questions pertaining to this quandary. Did a non-human being ever transform into or give birth to a human being? Flew could not answer this question in the affirmative and still retain credibility, in light of common sense, as well as the Law of Biogenesis. So, he rightly answered in the negative (Flew and Warren, 1977, p. 248). When pressed further about the implications of his admission, unwilling to concede God, Flew moved into the realm of irrationality. He stated:

> The position is that there are of course lots of cases where you can say without hesitation: "It is a lion, it is a horse, it is a man or it is not a

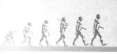

The Law of Biogenesis
vs. Evolution [Part III]

man." But it is, it seems to me a consequence of evolutionary theory that species **shade off into one another**. Hence when you are confronted by marginal cases, you cannot say this is **definitely human** or this is **not definitely human** (p. 25, emp. added).

So, there are creatures that are neither human nor non-human? As Warren stated in his rebuttal, such an illogical position denies the firmly established Law of Excluded Middle. As long as a "human" is precisely defined, everything is either human or not human. It is logically impossible to be neither human nor non-human. The more Warren pressed Flew on this matter, the more illogical Flew was required to become in order to hold to his position.

In his final speech on Monday night, he shocked the audience when he stated: "About whether I have met anyone who was not unequivocally either human or non-human: yes, I am afraid I have. I have met people who were very senile. I have also met people who were mad.... Can we say that these former people are people any longer?" (p. 65). Senile and mad **people** are non-humans? There are several problems with such a position. First, common sense dictates that such people are still human. Second, as long as "human" is precisely defined, the Law of Excluded Middle still applies. Third, Flew tacitly (certainly unconsciously) acknowledged that the "senile" and "mad" are actually human by using the word "people" in conjunction with them. "I have met **people** who were very senile. I have also met **people** who were mad." Fourth, notice that his argument is that such people may be considered non-human. He does not say that they are neither human nor non-human. "Can we say that these former people are **people any longer?**" He therefore admitted, unwittingly, that any being can be defined as human or non-human, even if his definition of a human is a ridiculous one. [NOTE: Flew's examples (i.e., senility and madness), even if they were erroneously conceded as legitimate examples of Darwinian evolution, were actually counterproductive to his case, since they would only illustrate that digression occurs in evolution, rather than progression.]

The bottom line is that every being is either human or non-human. In order for evolution to be true, a non-human had to give rise to a

human at some point in the past—either by transformation or birth. Based on the scientific evidence, neither is possible. And yet, there is no other option for the evolutionist, unless he contends that the first human just popped intact into existence spontaneously—like a fairy or like a dwarf springing from the ground. And yet this assertion would violate the First Law of Thermodynamics (see chapter two), the Law of Biogenesis, and, of course, reason itself. Life comes from life of its own kind. Period.

Even the evolutionary textbooks admit as much. Concerning the reproduction of living organisms, Prentice Hall's textbook, *Life Science*, states: "Another characteristic of organisms is the ability to reproduce, or produce offspring that are **similar to the parents**. For example, robins lay eggs that develop into young robins that **closely resemble their parents**" (Coolidge-Stolz, et al., 2005, p. 35, emp. added). Robins make robins. There may be small differences in color, height, beak size, etc. However, the offspring **is still a robin**—not a shark and not a hawk. **Evolutionary theory is not in keeping with the scientific evidence.** However, the biblical model, once again, is in perfect harmony with the scientific evidence. God, the Being Who wrote the Law of Biogenesis, created life (Genesis 2:7; Acts 17:25) and made it to produce after its kind (Genesis 1:11,24). [NOTE: See chapter eight for more on this matter.]

Supernatural Creation: A Viewpoint Which Makes "Scientific" People Uncomfortable

It is abundantly clear that many in the scientific community refuse to accept supernatural creation as a possibility for the origin of life, because they consider such a position to be "unscientific." Sullivan said, "So far as the **actual evidence** goes, this [the Law of Biogenesis—JM] is still the **only possible conclusion**. But since it is a conclusion that seems to lead back to some supernatural creative act, it is a conclusion that **scientific men** find very difficult of acceptance" (p. 94, emp. added). Wald agreed, stating that

[m]ost modern biologists, having reviewed with satisfaction the downfall of the spontaneous generation hypothesis, yet unwilling to accept the alternative belief in special creation, are left with nothing. I think a **scientist** has no choice but to approach the origin of life through a hypothesis of spontaneous generation (1954, p. 290, emp. added).

Jastrow added his agreement to the throng, stating that, "At present, science has no satisfactory answer to the question of the origin of life on the earth. Perhaps the appearance of life on the earth is a miracle. **Scientists** are reluctant to accept that view, but their choices are limited" (1977, pp. 62-63, emp. added). Why is it that many such naturalistic scientists claim that supernatural creation is somehow unscientific?

The answer is that supernatural creation cannot be directly observed or tested (at least today), and thus is not open to direct scientific study. Evolutionary geologist of the University of Wyoming, Jonathan Hoffman, said that, "[A] scientific theory is testable and falsifiable.... '[I]ntelligent design' does not meet these criteria" (2005). "Houston, we have a problem." Even if that were true (and it is not), it is clear that evolution and abiogenesis certainly do not meet these same criteria. As discussed earlier, evolutionists admit that they do not know how life could have come about. How can something be tested and falsified when no one knows how it could have happened in the first place?

Is there any way to be certain as to how life originated? There **is** an answer to that question. One can look at the scientific evidence, and in keeping with the Law of Rationality, without bias and preconceived notions and warrantless assumptions, draw and accept the conclusions that are warranted from that evidence. What does the evidence say? All scientific investigation has led to the conclusion that in nature life **does not** spontaneously generate and that life gives rise to life of its kind, without exception. If the scientific evidence indicates that that is how **nature** operates, then by implication, life's origin and propagation must be explained by something that is **super**-nature—i.e., deity. If life cannot create itself, according to the Law of Biogenesis, Someone must have created it. But Who?

An analysis of the created order reveals evidence for many of the characteristics of the Creator of life. An examination of the Bible reveals that Nature's God is the God of the Bible, Whose characteristics, unlike the gods conjured up by mankind, line up perfectly with the characteristics of the natural order. Also, the Bible contains several characteristics that prove it to be beyond the writing capability of humans (i.e., it must be of divine origin), including its scientific foreknowledge and medical acumen [see Butt, 2007 for an investigation of some of the evidence on this topic], and that Book of divine origin claims to be the writings of a particular God—Jehovah. Putting all of this evidence together results in the conclusion that there is a God, and He is the God of the Bible. In the Bible, that God tells us how life originated and propagates itself (Genesis 1:11,24; 2:7; Acts 17:25; Exodus 20:11), and its explanation harmonizes perfectly with the Law of Biogenesis.

Summary

If it could be said that the Law of Biogenesis contradicts the scientific evidence, it would be false. However, such is not the case. It is in keeping with **all** the evidence. Consider though, that if one rejects the Creation model, the Law of Biogenesis **must** be false, since without the Creation model, life had to come from non-life—in violation of that law. The atheistic evolutionist's conclusion: all of the scientific evidence over the centuries which has proven, according to the evolutionists themselves, the impossibility of abiogenesis, should be discarded and blind belief in a theory which has no conclusive scientific support should be promoted.

One wonders why some "scientists" are unscientific in their view of origins. Why pick the view that is, by their own admission, "impossible"? Why not look at the scientific evidence and allow it to lead to a conclusion that is in keeping with that evidence—regardless of whether or not one wishes to accept it, and regardless of whether the ultimate Cause of life can be directly observed? Would not such an approach be the reasonable one? Would not such an approach be the scientific one? Why should the **assumption** be made that there is no Creator? Recognizing the existence of a Creator allows for an

explanation of the origin of life that is in keeping with the scientific evidence—unlike abiogenesis.

Recall renowned British philosopher Antony Flew. After decades of promoting atheism, he finally decided at the end of his life to accept the evidence and concede the existence of a Supreme Being. He wrote, "The only satisfactory explanation for the origin of such 'end-directed, self-replicating' life as we see on earth is an infinitely intelligent Mind" (Flew and Varghese, 2007, p. 132). While his willingness to stand against the overwhelming tide of false science in becoming somewhat of a deist is certainly commendable, coming to such a conclusion should not be difficult. An unbiased examination of the scientific evidence on the matter **shouts** the truth to the unbiased mind. Ironically, in the debate mentioned above, Christian philosopher Thomas B. Warren laid out evidence that conclusively proved the existence of God to Antony Flew 30 years prior to his finally beginning to accept the evidence (Flew and Warren, 1977).

Evolution is not in harmony with **true** science. Creation, however, **is**. If abiogenesis is **not** true according to science, special creation, which does not contradict the Law of Biogenesis, must, **of necessity**, be true. Science, once again, is the friend of God and His Word and the enemy of the atheist.

Science vs. Evolution

Common Quibble

- "You Say the Creation Model Harmonizes with the Law of Biogenesis, but Doesn't John 12:24 Contradict It?" [See Appendix 4.d]

Review Questions

1) What fundamental assumption leads to the naturalist's conclusion that abiogenesis must be possible?
2) In what way is biogenesis being "demoted" by some scientists, and what is the basis for that demotion?
3) According to the Law of Biogenesis, what two things does life come from?
4) Concerning the Law of Biogenesis, how are the words "nature," "only from life," and "that of its kind" relevant to the Creation/evolution controversy?
5) From whence came life, according to evolutionary theory?
6) What makes many scientists uncomfortable with the Law of Biogenesis?
7) What passages prove that the Law of Biogenesis is in harmony with the Bible?
8) If in nature, life comes only from life and that of its kind, where did life have to come from originally?

Chapter 8

Genetics vs. Evolution

Introduction

Gregor Mendel is known by many today as the "Father of Genetics" (Considine, 1976, p. 1155). His work led to the series of genetic principles known as "Mendel's laws" (Davis and Kenyon, 1989, p. 60). After his work was published in the *Transactions of the Natural History Society of Brünn*, his work was left essentially untouched and unknown for some 35 years, until other well-known geneticists conducted research which cited his. One of those— Hugo de Vries, a Dutch evolutionary botanist—is credited with having discovered the existence of genetic mutations.

Gregor Mendel

The Evolution of Evolution

In chapter seven, we saw that the Law of Biogenesis indicates that in nature, life must come from life **of its kind**. That revelation, while macroscopic in its application to biogenesis, is in keeping with the evidence at the genetic level as well, and provides further support for that important concept: life reproduces according to its kind.

Darwin's theory of evolution has, itself, evolved over the decades. With further scientific investigation into the legitimacy of Darwin's theory, time and again, evolutionists have been forced to admit that the current version of evolution cannot do what they previously thought it could. It never completely lines up with the evidence. The alleged evolutionary timeline, therefore, must be revised constantly: dates change as to when various animals lived in the distant past; the order of evolutionary development is endlessly revised; new theories attempting to explain why various animals developed particular body parts are constantly being developed. The theory of evolution evolves.

And truly, the evolution of evolution is not a process that has been in effect for only a few decades. Evolution itself did not originate with Charles Darwin. Forms of evolution have been considered for **millennia**, at least as far back as the 600s B.C., with Thales and his Milesian school and the Ionian school (Conford, 1957). And for millennia, those ideas have had to be continually revised to stay in keeping with the latest scientific understanding.

While it is true that one should expect scientific theories to be revised to a certain extent over time—revisions amounting to fine-tuning—the evolutionary model is not merely revised. It periodically requires complete overhauls in broad, fundamental areas of the theory that evolutionists had previously proclaimed as established fact (cf. Thompson, 1981; www.apologeticspress.org). Recall the words of Hoyle and Wickramasinghe: we should "be suspicious of a theory if more and more hypotheses are needed to support it" (1981, p. 135). The Alcoholics Anonymous definition of "insanity" comes to mind: doing the same thing over and over, but expecting different results. At some point, when attempts to prove a theory result in multiple,

Charles Darwin

successive roadblocks, the sane person must surely ponder, "Maybe we should scrap this theory and start over."

Regardless, Darwin came along at the right time in history for evolutionary theory to "take off" and gain followers. This circumstance was due to various reasons, not the least of which is surely the fact that he gave the irreligious a "respectable" reason to reject God. The result: Darwin is typically considered the "Father" of evolution.

Natural Selection and Neo-Darwinism

As is implied by the title of Darwin's famous book (i.e., *The Origin of Species by means of Natural Selection...*), the fundamental premise of Darwinian evolution was originally natural selection. Natural selection is the idea that nature selects those species that are most "fit" or suited to a particular environment for survival. Those species which are not as well-suited, and which do not migrate to environments more conducive to their anatomy, will die out. That idea is largely true and observable, and the creationist has no problem with it. It does not contradict the evidence or the Creation model.

The problem is that Darwin believed natural selection could be the means by which his evolutionary theory could happen—the mechanism that would accommodate the idea that all forms of life came about from previously existing, less complex life, starting with a single cell eons ago. But while natural selection might filter the unfit from a given population, it is not capable of **creating** anything—especially species that are not only complex, but more complex than their ancestors. John Sanford, co-inventor of the "Biolistic Particle Delivery System" (i.e., the "gene gun"), is one of the few elite individuals with the title of "population geneticist." His Ph.D. in plant breeding and genetics and years of further research in genetic engineering, as well as his position as a professor at Cornell University, placed him on the front lines of the scientific community in gathering evidence for and against natural selection and evolution. His work in plant genetics led him from being an ardent atheistic evolutionist to being a creationist.

In his book, *Genetic Entropy & the Mystery of the Genome*, Sanford explained:

> For many people, including many biologists, natural selection is like a magic wand. There seems to be no limit to what one can imagine it accomplishing. This extremely naïve perspective toward natural selection is pervasive.... [N]atural selection is *not* a magic wand but is a very real phenomenon, it has very real capabilities and very real *limitations*. It is not all-powerful (2008, p. 46, italics in orig.).

Scientists have realized today that Darwin was wrong. Natural selection alone would not suffice to cause evolution to occur. Evolutionary paleontologist Stephen Jay Gould of Harvard University once explained, "The essence of Darwinism lies in a single phrase: natural selection is the creative force of evolutionary change. No one denies that selection will play a negative role in eliminating the unfit. Darwinian theories require that it **create** the fit as well" (1977, p. 28, emp. added). Therein lies the problem. Evolutionists recognize today that they cannot even **claim** that natural selection could **create** the fit. Dutch evolutionary botanist, Hugo de Vries, long ago said, "Natural selection may explain the **survival** of the fittest, but it cannot explain the **arrival** of the fittest" (1905, pp. 825-826, emp. added).

Bottom line: evolutionists have realized that natural selection cannot provide the mechanism required for evolutionary change. Enter neo-Darwinism, the version of evolution that is now en vogue. Neo-Darwinism, also known as the "Primary Axiom" (Sanford, 2008), attempts to revise Darwinism by contending that natural selection coupled with genetic mutations—random DNA accidents—provide the mechanism for evolution to occur. In the words of molecular and cell biologist Jonathan Wells of the Center for Science and Culture at the Discovery Institute in Seattle, "It was not until the 1930s that Darwinian evolution and Mendelian genetics were combined in what became known as the neo-Darwinian synthesis. According to neo-Darwinian theory, traits are passed on by genes that reside on microscopic thread-like structures in the cell called chromosomes, and **new traits arise from accidental genetic mutations**" (2011, p. 18, emp. added). According to neo-Darwinism, random mutations could accidentally create new species over time, and natural selection

could eliminate the unfit ones, leaving the better, more evolved species in existence.

Concerning neo-Darwinism, molecular biologist John McFadden wrote: "Over millions of years, organisms will evolve by selection of mutant offspring which are fitter than their parents. **Mutations are therefore the elusive source of the variation that Darwin needed to complete his theory of evolution**. They provide the raw material for all evolutionary change" (2000, p. 65, emp. added). Years ago, George Gaylord Simpson and his co-authors said, "Mutations are the ultimate raw materials for evolution" (1957, p. 430). One genetics textbook put it this way: "Mutations constitute the raw material for evolution; they are the basis for the variability in a population on which natural (or artificial) selection acts to preserve those combinations of genes best adapted to a particular environment" (Snyder, et al., 1985, p. 353, parenthetical item in orig.). Is it true that mutations can provide the raw material and mechanism for Darwinian evolution to occur over millions of years? Do mutations eliminate the need for a supernatural Source to explain the origin of species?

Creating Information: A Prerequisite for Evolution

Recall Stephen Meyer, origin-of-life biologist and doctoral graduate of Cambridge University. In his book on the origin of genetic information, he discussed one of the greatest discoveries of the twentieth century—the structure of the DNA molecule by James Watson and Francis Crick. He noted that "when Watson and Crick discovered the structure of DNA, they also discovered that DNA stores information using a four-character chemical alphabet. Strings of precisely sequenced chemicals called nucleotide bases store and transmit the assembly instructions—the information—for building the crucial protein molecules and machines the cell needs to survive" (2009, Ch. 1). Information is packed into our genes, and its transfer during reproduction is critical. Without the transfer of information, there would be no such thing as life.

Information scientist, professor, and control engineer Werner Gitt, retired director of the Information Technology Division at the German Federal Institute of Physics and Technology, noted that, "The concept of 'information' is not only of prime importance for informatics theories and communication techniques, but it is a fundamental quantity in such wide-ranging sciences as cybernetics, linguistics, biology, history, and theology. Many scientists therefore justly regard information as the third fundamental entity alongside matter and energy" (2007, Ch. 3). Meyer argues that "[o]ur actions show that we not only value information, but that we regard it as a real entity, on par with matter and energy" (2009, Ch. 1). Indeed, "[a]t the close of the nineteenth century, most biologists thought life consisted solely of matter and energy. But after Watson and Crick, biologists came to recognize the importance of a third fundamental entity in living things: information" (Ch. 3).

How does this third "fundamental entity in living things" relate to the evolution question? In order for evolution to occur, information would have to be created—at the beginning of life and at every macroevolutionary jump between living kinds. This presents a problem for evolution, which Bernd-Olaf Kuppers, biophysicist, professor of natural philosophy, and director of the Frege Centre for Structural Sciences at the University of Jena, summarized: "The problem of the origin of life is clearly basically equivalent to the problem of the origin of biological information" (1990, p. 170). In the book, *In the Beginning was Information*, Gitt makes the compelling argument that "[t]he question 'How did life originate?' which interests us all, is inseparably linked to the question 'Where did the information come from?'... All evolutionary views are fundamentally unable to answer this crucial question" (Ch. 6). Neil Shubin, paleontologist and professor of organismal biology and anatomy at the University of Chicago wrote:

> I can share with you one true law that all of us can agree upon. This law is so profound that most of us take it completely for granted. Yet it is the starting point for almost everything we do in paleontology, developmental biology, and genetics. This biological "law of everything" is that every living thing on the planet had parents. Every person you've

ever known has biological parents, as does every bird, salamander, or shark you have ever seen.... To put it in a more precise form: every living thing sprang from some **parental genetic information** (2009, p. 174, emp. added).

The scientific evidence indicates that genetic information is always passed from parents. It does not spring into existence. So how did it originate? How **could** it originate, without an initial Parent capable of creating genetic information?

Obviously, the existence of genetic information, its transfer from parent to offspring, and the mechanism—the software and the hardware—by which it transfers are critical to life. More importantly, their origin must be explained, since the Creation/evolution debate hinges on that explanation. Under the evolutionary model, the first life had to be information rich, though being the product of non-living matter, and from that life, an immense amount of other information had to be "written" into the genome over time through mutations during reproduction in order for humans to be in existence today. And yet, in the words of Gitt, "There is no known law of nature, no known process, and no known sequence of events which can cause information to originate by itself in matter" (Ch. 6).

> "There is no known law of nature, no known process, and no known sequence of events which can cause information to originate by itself in matter."

While there are proposals attempting to explain the origin of the genetic code through natural means, according to Gitt, those proposals are "purely imaginary models. It has not been shown empirically how information can arise in matter" (Ch. 6). Naturalism simply cannot explain the origin of information. Gitt continues, "The basic flaw of all evolutionary views is the origin of the information in living beings. It has never been shown that a coding system and semantic information could originate by itself in a material medium, and the information theorems predict that this will never be possible. A purely material origin of life is thus precluded" (Ch. 11). Meyer explained, "[S]elf-organizational laws or processes of necessity cannot generate—as

opposed to merely transmit—new information" (2009, Ch. 15). After reviewing the many attempts over the years to explain the origin of information, Meyer summarized:

> Every attempt to explain the origin of biological information either failed because it **transferred** the problem elsewhere or "succeeded" only by presupposing **unexplained sources** of information.... Every major origin-of-life scenario—whether based on chance, necessity, or the combination—failed to explain the origin of specified information. **Thus, ironically, origin-of-life research itself confirms that undirected chemical processes do not produce large amounts of specified information starting from purely physical or chemical antecedents** (2009, Ch. 15, emp. added).

Several years ago, evolutionary scientists gathered in Mainz, Germany and discussed some of the problems that had yet to be solved by naturalists (and still have not been solved today) regarding origins. Klaus Dose of the Institute for Biochemistry at Johannes Gutenberg University wrote concerning the findings of the seventh "International Conference on the Origins of Life":

> A further puzzle remains, namely the question of the origin of biological information, i.e., the information residing in our genes today.... The Mainz report may have an equally important historical impact, because for the first time it has now been determined unequivocally by a large number of scientists that all evolutionary theses that living systems developed from poly-nucleotides which originated spontaneously, are **devoid of any empirical base** (1983, pp. 968-969, emp. added).

In other words, evolution requires the spontaneous generation of information (and life), and yet no scientist has any empirical evidence that such a thing could happen. But evolution **requires** the spontaneous generation of information. Without such a process, naturalistic evolution has no mechanism for the initial generation of information at the onset of life or for inter-kind transformation.

Mutations, Manuals, and New Information

Though neo-Darwinism has been proposed as the solution to rectify the inadequacy of natural selection in causing macroevolution, in

reality, it has its own problems as well. Simply put, genetic mutations do not create **new** raw material or information—which is necessary for the kind of change required by evolutionary theory. Mutations cannot explain the origin of new information. Speaking to that issue, British engineer and physicist Alan Hayward, said years ago:

> [M]utations do not appear to bring progressive changes. Genes seem to be **built** so as to allow changes to occur within certain narrow limits, and to prevent those limits from being crossed. To oversimplify a little: mutations very easily produce new varieties within a species, and might occasionally produce a new (though similar) species, but—despite enormous efforts by experimenters and breeders—**mutations seem unable to produce entirely new forms of life** (1985, p. 55, emp. added).

Gould said, concerning mutations, "A mutation doesn't produce major **new raw material**. You don't make a new species by mutating the species.... That's a common idea people have; that evolution is due to random mutations. **A mutation is not the cause of evolutionary change**" (1980, emp. added). A mutation does not "produce major new raw material"? What does that mean?

Sanford likens the genome to an instruction manual for making human beings. In his analogy, letters correspond to nucleotides, words correspond to small clusters of nucle-otides, "which combine to form genes (the *chapters* of our manual), which

> "A mutation doesn't produce major new raw material."

combine to form chromosomes (the *volumes* of our manual), which combine to form the whole genome (the entire *library*)" (2008, p. 2, italics in orig.). In the printing, re-typing, or digital copying of a book, errors—or mutations—will sometimes appear when you examine the finished product. For example, individual words could be garbled—a few letters of a word could be changed to other letters, termed codon errors in genetics. Duplication could occur—the idea that words, sentences, and even entire paragraphs could be duplicated somewhere within the book. Translocation could occur—where sections from one part of the book are moved and inserted elsewhere in the book. Deletion could occur—where segments of the book are simply lost.

Though these kinds of errors or mutations (and others) can occur, no new material is written when they do. No **new information** has been added to the book. A new sentence has not been written into the story. The problem with evolutionary theory is that it requires new sentences and even chapters to have been written through mutations in the genetic "book." In fact, it requires sequels of the book to write themselves into existence through random mutation.

In answer to the question, "Can new information originate through mutations?" Gitt responded, "This idea is central in representations of evolution, but mutations can only cause changes in **existing information**. There can be no increase in information, and in general the results are injurious. New blueprints for new functions or new organs cannot arise; mutations cannot be the source of new (creative) information" (Gitt, Ch. 11, emp. added, parenthetical item in orig.). Meyer explains, "[N]atural selection can 'select' only what random mutations first produce. And for the evolutionary process to produce new forms of life, random mutations must first have produced new genetic information for building novel proteins" (2009, Ch. 9). And again, that simply does not happen.

> [M]utations of the kind that macroevolution **doesn't** need (namely, viable genetic mutations in DNA expressed late in development) do occur, but those that it **does** need (namely, beneficial body plan mutations expressed early in development) apparently **don't occur**. According to Darwin (1859, p. 108) natural selection cannot act until favorable variations arise in a population. Yet there is **no evidence** from developmental genetics that the kind of variations required by neo-Darwinism—namely, favorable body plan mutations—**ever occur**.... [M]utations in DNA alone cannot account for the morphological changes required to build a new body plan (Meyer, 2004, emp. added).

Mutation simply "does not constitute an adequate causal explanation of the origination of biological form in the higher taxonomic groups" (Meyer, 2004).

Meyer summarized the problem for neo-Darwinism:

> Neo-Darwinism seeks to explain the origin of new information, form, and structure as a result of selection acting on randomly arising

variation at a very low level within the biological hierarchy, namely, within the genetic text. Yet major morphological innovations depend on a specificity of arrangement at a much higher level of the organizational hierarchy, a level that DNA alone does not determine. Yet if DNA is not wholly responsible for body plan morphogenesis, then DNA sequences can mutate indefinitely, without regard to realistic probabilistic limits, and still not produce a new body plan. Thus, the mechanism of natural selection acting on random mutations in DNA **cannot *in principle* generate novel body plans** (Meyer, 2004, italics in orig., emp. added).

In the words of Sanford:

> [E]ven when ignoring deleterious mutations, mutation/selection cannot create a single gene within the human evolutionary timescale. When deleterious mutations are factored back in, we see that mutation/selection cannot create a single gene, **ever**. This is overwhelming evidence against the Primary Axiom. *In my opinion this constitutes what is essentially a formal proof that the Primary Axiom is false* (p. 139, emp. and italics in orig.).

Michael Behe, biochemist and Professor of Biological Sciences at Lehigh University, points out that some microorganisms have been shown to be able to rapidly adapt to new environments. However, in doing so, those organisms never develop new internal functions. According to Behe, their adaptations amount, not to innovation, but merely fine-tuning (2007).

> "[M]utation/selection cannot create a single gene, **ever**. This is overwhelming evidence against the Primary Axiom."

So in the words of Gould, mutations do not "produce major new raw material." They simply change something that already exists. They alter what is already present. They are variations within types of already existing genes. They might cause a fly to have extra wings, a fish to have extra eyes, or a person to have an extra toe; but mutations cannot create a new kind of creature. A mutation would not cause a wing to appear on a creature unless the creature already had wings in its genetic code. If a fish does not already have antlers in its genes, it is not going to grow them. If a dog does not have webbed duck feet or feathers in its genes, it will

never grow them. If a person does not have tank treads in his genes, he will never be able to roll over to his neighbor's house, regardless of how long he (or his progeny) lives and mutates. Neo-Darwinian evolution simply cannot happen. Sanford lamented:

> Very regrettably, evolutionists have treated two very different phenomenon, *adaptation to environments* and *evolution of higher life forms*, as if they were the same thing. We do not need to be geniuses to see that these are different issues. Adaptation can routinely be accomplished by loss of information or even developmental degeneration (loss of organs). However, development of higher life forms (representing more specified complexity) always requires a large increase in information (p. 202, italics in orig.).

And Darwinian evolution cannot provide it.

Information: If It's Not a Product of Naturalistic Processes, Then...

East German scientist J. Peil wrote, "Information is neither a physical nor a chemical principle like energy and matter, even though the latter are required as carriers" (as quoted in Gitt, 2007, Ch. 3). The late American mathematician Norbert Wiener, previously professor of mathematics at M.I.T., graduate of Harvard University, and considered to be the originator of the field of cybernetics, long ago said, "Information is information, not matter or energy. No materialism which does not admit this can survive at the present day" (1965, p. 132). What does that truth imply about information?

In the words of Gitt in what he calls

> **Theorem I:**
> "The fundamental quantity information is a non-material (mental) entity. It is not a property of matter, so that purely material processes are fundamentally precluded as sources of information."

"Theorem 1," "[t]he fundamental quantity information is a non-material (mental) entity. **It is not a property of matter, so that purely material processes are fundamentally precluded as sources of information**"

(Ch. 3, emp. added). He further explains, "Information is always based on the will of a sender who issues the information.... Information only arises through an intentional, volitional act" (Ch. 3). "[I]t is clear that the information present in living organisms requires an intelligent source.... Any model for the origin of life (and of information) based solely on physical and/or chemical processes, is inherently false" (Ch. 4, parenthetical item in orig.). Gitt proposes Theorem 29 as a summary of that truth: "Every piece of creative information represents some mental effort and can be traced to a personal idea-giver who exercised his own free will, and who is endowed with an intelligent mind" (Ch. 8). In other words, "New information can only originate in a creative thought process" (Ch. 8).

> "Information only arises through an intentional, volitional act."

What about the findings from computerized evolutionary algorithms and ribozyme-engineering experiments? Don't they prove neo-Darwinian evolution could happen? Meyer responds:

> [M]inds can produce biologically relevant structures and forms of information, but without mind or intelligence little, if any, information arises.... [I]ntelligent agents can produce information. And since all evolutionary algorithms require preexisting sources of information provided by designing minds, they show the power—if not the necessity—of intelligent design.... [R]ibozyme-engineering experiments demonstrate the power—if not, again, the need for—intelligence to produce information—in this case, the information necessary to enhance the function of RNA enzymes.... Undirected materialistic causes have not demonstrated the capacity to generate significant amounts of specified information. At the same time, conscious intelligence has repeatedly shown itself capable of producing such information. It follows that mind—conscious, rational, intelligent agency—what philosophers call "agent causation," now stands as the only cause known to be capable of generating large amounts of specified information starting from a nonliving state (2009, Ch. 15).

Radiologist Henry Quastler, who pioneered the use of isotopes to study cell kinetics and "was one of the first to apply Information Theory to biology" (Ducoff, 2007), long ago stated, "[C]reation of information

Science vs. Evolution

is habitually associated with conscious activity” (Quastler, 1964, p. 16). If this be the case—if all the evidence points to an intelligent Designer for the origin of information—why reject the evidence? “Whatever information is—whether thought or an elaborate arrangement of matter—one thing seems clear. What humans recognize as information certainly *originates* from thought—from conscious or intelligent activity” (Meyer, 2009, Ch. 1, italics in orig.).

But Still...Couldn't it Happen?

Even if genetic mutation **could** sporadically provide new information, there are other, even more significant issues. Meyer explains, “[A]ny minimally complex protocell resembling cells we have today would have required not only genetic information, but a sizable preexisting suite of proteins for processing that information” (2009, Ch. 9). And what's more,

> scientists investigating the origin of life must now explain the origin of at least three key features of life. First, they must explain the origin of the system for storing and encoding digital information in the cell, DNA's capacity to store digitally encoded information. Second, they must explain the origin of the large amount of specified complexity or functionally specified information in DNA. Third, they must explain the origin of the integrated complexity—the functional interdependence of parts—of the cell's information-processing system (2009, Ch. 5).

Sanford points out further how Darwinian evolution would still not be possible with sporadic instances of new information:

> I believe the “going down” aspect of the genome is subject to concrete analysis. Such analysis persuasively argues that *net* information must be declining. If this is true [and the primary focus of his book is to illustrate that it is—JM], then even if it could be shown that there were specific cases where new information *might* be synthesized via mutation/selection, it would still be meaningless since such new information would promptly then begin to degenerate again. The net direction would still be *down*, and complex genomes could never have arisen spontaneously. If the genome is actually degenerating, it is...bad news for evolutionary theory. If mutation/selection cannot *preserve* the information already within the genome, it is difficult to

114

imagine how it could have *created* all that information in the first place! We cannot rationally speak of genome-building when there is a net loss of information every generation! Halting degeneration is just a small prerequisite step before the much more difficult question of *information-building* can reasonably be opened for discussion (pp. 105-106, italics in orig.).

Wells argues that

even if scientists eventually observe the origin of a new species by natural selection, the observation would not mean that natural selection can also explain the origin of **significantly new organs or body plans**. But the fact that scientists have not observed even the first step in macroevolution means that "evolution's smoking gun" is still missing. Despite the lack of direct evidence for speciation [i.e., the origin of new species—JM] by natural selection, Darwin's followers still assume that he was essentially correct and regard changes within existing species as evidence for their theory (p. 13, emp. added).

Once again, speculation and conjecture without supporting evidence rule the day in evolutionary circles and textbooks. All the while, mounds of evidence exist which indicate that new information is not possible through genetic mutation. So neo-Darwinian evolution is not possible.

Genetic Entropy: The Unavoidable Trend

Mutations are, by definition, "errors"—mistakes in the replication of DNA (cf. Ayala, 1978, 239[3]:56-69). There are three possible kinds of mutations: bad, good, and neutral (i.e., those that have no net effect on a species one way or the other)—none of which add new raw material or information to the genome. Evolution hinges on the idea that beneficial mutations must be the trend, since evolution requires a **progression** in species (and those mutations must simultaneously add new raw material in order to evolve a new species).

However, in truth, the scientific evidence indicates that this trend is not the case. Renowned geneticist of Stanford University, Luigi Cavalli-Sforza, head of the International Human Genome Diversity Project, said, "Genetic mutations are spontaneous, chance changes, which are rarely beneficial, and more often have no effect or a deleterious one" (2000, p. 176, emp. added). Prominent evolutionary taxonomist, Ernst Mayr (professor emeritus of Harvard), wrote, "[T]he occurrence of beneficial mutations is rather rare" (2001, p. 98, emp. added). In fact, it has long been realized that, after eliminating the neutral mutations from the discussion, 99% of the remaining mutations are said to be actually harmful—not beneficial (Crow, 1997; Cartwright, 2000, p. 98; Winchester, 1951, p. 228; Martin, 1953, p. 100; Ayala, 1968, p. 1436; Morris, 1984, p. 203; Klotz, 1985, p. 181). This was recognized as long ago as 1950, when Nobel laureate and geneticist, Hermann J. Muller said, "The great majority of mutations, certainly well over 99%, are harmful in some way" (1950, 38:35, emp. added). Famous evolutionary geneticist of Rockefeller University, Theodosius Dobzhansky, admitted that beneficial mutations make up less than 1% of all mutations (as quoted in Davidheiser, 1969, p. 209).

Several decades of further research did not help matters. The late evolutionary geneticist of the University of Massachusetts in Amherst Lynn Margulis, and her co-author science writer Dorion Sagan, referenced Muller's historic work, emphasizing that "as was pointed out very early by Hermann J. Muller (1890-1967), the Nobel prizewinner who showed X-rays to be mutagenic in fruit flies, 99.9 percent of the mutations **are [still—JM] deleterious**. Even professional evolutionary biologists are hard put to find mutations, experimentally induced or spontaneous, that lead in a positive way to evolutionary change" (2002, pp. 11-12, emp. added). According to theoretical evolutionary geneticist Philip Gerrish of the University of New Mexico and Richard Lenski, experimental evolutionary biologist of Michigan State University, it seems that the best estimates for beneficial mutations are now "roughly one in a million" (1998, p. 132). Thomas Bataillon, evolutionary biologist of Aarhus University's Bioinformatics Research Centre, and Santiago Elena, molecular and evolutionary geneticist of the Institute of Molecular and Cellular Plant Biology in Spain, argue that the rate of beneficial mutations is so low that it cannot even be measured (Bataillon, 2000; Elena, et al., 1998). Behe even argues, based on a thorough examination of relevant evolutionary experiments over

the last few decades, that those mutations which are considered to be "beneficial" for an organism still typically involved a loss of function (i.e., a loss of genetic information)—not a gain. In the summary of his 2010 article in the *Quarterly Review of Biology*, he says, "The results of decades of experi-mental [sic] laboratory evolution studies strongly suggest that, at the molecular level, loss-of-FCT [i.c., loss of function—JM] and diminishing modification-of-function adaptive mutations predominate" (2010, p. 441). In truth, this circumstance should be expected, since mutations are, by definition, deviations from what would have occurred in the replication of DNA, if everything worked in the way that it should.

So mutations do not provide the progressive, beneficial trend required by evolution, but rather, reveal a **digressive** trend. Mutations, by and large, are deleterious, not beneficial to the genome. That is what the **scientific evidence** indicates—an avalanche of harmful mutations sweeping all species on the planet down the slope of deterioration, decay, and digression. This trend is in keeping with the Second Law of Thermodynamics—entropy is inevitable (see Sanford, 2008 for a decisive treatise on the truth of genetic entropy). The genome will inevitably deteriorate, not evolve. This trend is also supported by information theory (Gitt, 2007).

"Error catastrophe" is the term used to describe what happens when natural selection cannot adequately counter the loss of information that occurs due to deleterious mutations—a situation we are currently facing. During the final phase of degeneration, "mutational meltdown" occurs (Bernardes, 1996)—the "rapid collapse of the population and sudden extinction" of the species (Sanford, p. 220). Kevin Higgins and Michael Lynch, evolutionary biologists of Indiana University and the University of Oregon, respectively, argue that extinction is currently a significant risk for many mammals and other animals because of the existing state of deterioration in the genome due to mutations. "Under synchronous environmental fluctuations, the acceleration of extinction caused by mutation accumulation is striking.... [F]or a large globally dispersing metapopulation with mutation accumulation, the extinction

time is just slightly longer than 100 generations" (2001). There is no doubt that genetic entropy is the trend, not genetic organization.

Behe argues, "[N]ot only does Darwinism not have answers for how information got into the genome, it doesn't even have answers for how it could **remain** there" (as quoted in Sanford, 2008, back cover, emp. added). Genetic entropy prohibits it. No wonder Sanford wrote, "Degeneration is the precise *antithesis* of evolutionary theory. Therefore the reality of Genetic Entropy is positively fatal to Darwinism" (p. 206, italics in orig.). Expounding on that idea, he said:

> "[N]ot only does Darwinism not have answers for how information got into the genome, it doesn't even have answers for how it could remain there."

> If the genome must degenerate, then the Primary Axiom is wrong. It is not just implausible. It is not just unlikely. It is absolutely dead wrong. It is not just a false axiom. It is an unsupported and discredited hypothesis, and can be confidently rejected. Mutation/selection cannot stop the loss of genomic information, let alone *create* the genome! Why is this? It is because selection occurs on the level of the whole organism. It cannot stop the loss of information (which is immeasurably complex) due to mutation, and is happening on the molecular level. **It is like trying to fix a computer with a hammer** (p. 147, italics and emp. in orig.).

Due to entropy, the genetic trend is downward. But evolution demands an upward trend—not good for Darwinian evolution.

Consider again, however, that while deterioration destroys evolutionary theory, notice that the trend towards deterioration is in keeping with the Creation model, which argues that the genome was originally pristine in the Garden before sin entered the world, initiating the decay process (Romans 5:12; Psalm 102:25-27). The natural trend all around us is clearly that living creatures are being swept down the proverbial mountainside in an avalanche of entropy. Yet evolutionary theory irrationally postulates that the trend for the mindless, accidental evolution of species has actually been up the mountainside against an oppressive wall of tumbling snow.

Mutations: Not the Evolutionary Mechanism

No wonder, like Gould and Hayward, Margulis and Sagan strongly expressed their disagreement with the idea that genetic mutations could be the mechanism for evolution, as neo-Darwinism contends. They said, "[R]andom mutation, a small part of the evolutionary saga, has been dogmatically overemphasized" (2002, p. 15). "Many ways to induce mutations are known but none lead to new organisms. Mutation accumulation does not lead to new species or even to new organs or new tissues.... We show here that the major source of inherited variation is not random mutation" (2002, pp. 11-12, emp. added). Evolutionist Pierre-Paul Grassé, who was the chair of evolution at the Sorbonne in Paris for over 30 years, said, "No matter how numerous they may be, **mutations do not produce any kind of evolution**" (1977, p. 103, emp. added). Nobel laureate, Sir Ernst Chain, who is credited with having purified penicillin in such a way that it could be used as an antibiotic, said years ago, "To postulate...that the development and survival of the fittest is entirely a consequence of chance mutations... seems to me a hypothesis **based on no evidence and irreconcilable with the facts**" (1970, p. 25, emp. added). As we have seen, such profound statements are still relevant today.

Indeed, due to the nature of genetics, mutations simply do not provide a mechanism for Darwinian evolution to occur. In the words of

> "Without any naturalistic mechanism, evolution is not significantly different from any faith-based religion."

Sanford, "The demise of the Primary Axiom leaves evolutionary theory without any viable mechanism. Without any naturalistic mechanism, evolution is not significantly different from any faith-based religion" (2008, p. 206; cf. Houts, 2007). Neo-Darwinism has no mechanism for progressing towards new species, and the origin of the genetic code remains a mystery for naturalists. Recall the words of evolutionist Douglas Hofstadter:

> There are various theories on the origin of life. They all run aground on this most central of all central questions: "How did the Genetic Code, along with the mechanisms for its translation (ribosomes and

Science vs. Evolution

RNA molecules) originate?" For the moment, we will have to content ourselves with a sense of **wonder and awe rather than with an answer** (1980, p. 548, emp. added).

Writing in *Nature*, evolutionist John Maddox said, "[I]t is disappointing that the origin of the genetic code is **still as obscure** as the origin of life itself" (1994, 367:111, emp. added). The unfortunate truth is that so many, both theists and atheists alike, have been steamrolled into believing Darwinian religion by the naturalist crowd. Evolution has been thrust on the minds of children and touted as scientific fact for decades, when all the while, upon closer examination of the evidence, evolution is found to be baseless in its attempt to explain the origin of species. All the while, an explanation for the origin of the kinds of creatures we see on Earth is available that does not contradict the scientific evidence.

In the words of Stephen Hawking, "[T]he Universe is a machine governed by principles or laws—laws that can be understood by the human mind.... But what's really important is that these physical laws, as well as being unchangeable, are universal. They apply not just to the flight of the ball, but to the motion of a planet and **everything else in the Universe**" ("Curiosity...," 2011, emp. added). As with everything else in the law-abiding Universe, reproduction behaves in accordance with governing laws. Life produces according to its kind. The Bible, which articulates the Creation model in simple terms, stated long ago a truth that has stood the test of time and continues to be verified by modern science. God made living creatures and then established the ordinances which would govern their reproduction. The phrase "according to its kind" is used repeatedly (Genesis 1:11,12,21,24,25), highlighting the clear barriers that God set up between various forms of life—distinctions which evolutionary theory seeks to dissolve. Genesis 1:11-12 and 1:24 recount for us the general law that God wrote at the creation of the Universe regarding life and reproduction: plants and animals were to reproduce "according to their kind." That simple statement has profound import and denies the theory of evolution, which requires inter-kind jumps—prohibited by the evidence from genetics. [NOTE: The word "kind" was written in Genesis long before

120

the modern taxonomic categories developed. While there may be no direct equivalent to the present taxonomic system, the "family" of a creature may be the best parallel in most cases.]

Common Quibble

- "Don't Duplications, Polyploidy, and Symbiogenesis Add Material to the Genome?" [See Appendix 5.a]
- "Can't Order come from Disorder on Earth Due to the Sun?" [See Appendix 5.b]

Review Questions

1) What is "natural selection," and who is credited with originating the idea?
2) Natural selection may explain the survival of the fittest, but what does it not explain?
3) What is "neo-Darwinism"?
4) What is not produced by a mutation?
5) Based on numbers (3) and (4), what can be inferred about neo-Darwinism?
6) What kind of trend do mutations cause in our genome?
7) What kind of trend should be expected based on the evolutionary model?
8) What Bible passages support the evidence from genetics?

Chasms in the Evolutionary Pathway

If one were to decide one day to take a stroll down the path representing the naturalistic evolutionary timeline—starting with nothing and ending with everything—he would be stopped before he could begin. The evolutionary pathway is filled with gaping chasms that cannot be crossed without brushing aside the scientific evidence. Where did matter and energy originally come from? Where did the laws governing the natural realm come from? How did life come into being? How could the alleged simple life give rise to all of the complex life we see today? Recall the seven fundamental planks that comprise the foundation of naturalistic evolutionary theory from the Introduction. It is evident, from this brief look at several of the laws of science, that the first five fundamental planks of evolutionary theory are, in fact, chasms that lie in the path of naturalistic evolution that prohibit it from being true.

1) The Universe could not have spontaneously generated or be eternal. The First and Second Laws of Thermodynamics, as well as the Law of Causality, prohibit such phenomena.

2) Abiogenesis could not have occurred. The Law of Biogenesis, as well as the Laws of Probability and the Law of Causality, eliminate that option.

3) Macroevolution cannot account for the existence of the kinds of creatures on the Earth today, since inter-kind evolution contradicts the Law of Biogenesis and the nature of genetic mutation and information creation.

4) Neo-Darwinism cannot provide the mechanism for macroevolution, since genetic mutations do not add new information to the genome.

123

5) Humans and apes do not have a common ancestor, since such would require macroevolution which, again, contradicts the Law of Biogenesis and the laws governing genetics.

In order for atheism and naturalism to be true, each of the fundamental planks of naturalistic evolutionary theory must be true. If any one of those statements is shown to be unreasonable in light of the evidence, the entire evolutionary model collapses. As we have seen, the laws of science deny—not one—but five of the fundamental planks of cosmic evolution. The Creation model, on the other hand, stands in perfect harmony with the scientific evidence. [NOTE: The other two planks can be shown to be contradictory to the scientific evidence as well, but a presentation of that evidence is outside the scope of this book. See www.apologeticspress.org and DeYoung, 2005 for information addressing those planks.]

"Science"—In Need of a New Definition

Science, today, has been defined in such a way that a legitimate option—one that is not only in keeping with the evidence, but that is demanded by it—has been eliminated from the table of scientific discussion. And what's left on the table contradicts the evidence at every turn. Question: to skeptically minded individuals, after reading this book, can it be granted that it is at least **possible** that God exists and created the Universe? Are there certain phenomena that cannot be adequately explained through natural means; phenomena which point to the supernatural, or that can at least be better explained through the supernatural? If the answer is "yes," and a fundamental goal of science is to determine the truth, then why has God been completely eliminated from the scientific discussion? This is an important question: one that reveals a certain irrational bias against God and towards naturalism. To completely eliminate the question of God from the table, as though He is not even a possible option, is hardly a reasonable approach to finding truth. It is an erroneous, unscientific, and even foolish approach. If God exists and the Bible is His Word, then evolution is false and much time and effort is being wasted in

an effort to substantiate it. Furthermore, if the scientific evidence is interpreted through the lens of the Creation model, completely different conclusions will be drawn. Creationists have long tried to highlight the fact that we do not disagree with the evidence from science; rather, we disagree with the interpretation of that evidence by naturalists. As with many findings, the evidence can be interpreted various ways based on the perspective of the individual examining the evidence—and especially on the model or theory to which he subscribes. Why not interpret the evidence in a way that harmonizes with **all** of the evidence and that does not ignore or marginalize valid evidence simply because that evidence does not fit the model being used?

Would it not be reasonable to re-define "science" in such a way that no potential option is eliminated from consideration based on the faulty assumption of naturalism? After all, men of science through the millenia believed that science pointed to God. They did not hold to the assumption of naturalism, and scientific progress was in no way hindered. In fact, quite the contrary is true. Their work rocketed science and technology to unprecedented heights. Only since the spread of empiricism and naturalism has "science" been defined in such a way that precludes God. If the scientific evidence points to Something supernatural, why not be allowed as scientists to follow the evidence wherever it leads, as did the fathers of science?

Just because one cannot empirically observe something happening, or empirically observe someone doing something, it does not follow that one cannot use observation to determine who did what, how they did it, when they did it, where they did it, and what they did it with. Forensic scientists engage in this process every day. Indirect evidence is a legitimate source of scientific information, and ironically, evolutionists admit this—at least, when it supports their theory. Consider Richard Dawkins' comments concerning evolution. In his 2009 book, *The Greatest Show on Earth*, he acknowledged that in his previous books "the evidence for evolution itself was nowhere explicitly set out" (p. vii). This gap he intended to rectify. To what evidence did he point that he erroneously claimed proved evolution

to be "a fact—as incontrovertible a fact as any in science" (p. vii)? Indirect evidence. He stated:

> Obviously, the vast majority of evolutionary change is invisible to direct eye-witness observation. Most of it happened before we were born, and in any case it is usually too slow to be seen during an individual's lifetime.... With evolution, as with continental drift, inference after the event is all that is available to us, for the obvious reason that we don't exist until after the event. But do not for one nanosecond underestimate the power of such inference (p. 16).

He further wrote, "I shall never again be tempted to give eyewitness testimony an automatic preference over indirect scientific inference" (p. 15). While the rational individual will be very careful not to draw more than can be drawn from indirect evidence (unlike naturalistic evolutionists), that indirect evidence can be a legitimate source of scientific information. This type of evidence is precisely what creationists have long argued to be in support of the Creation model (cf. Romans 1:20). Consider: if evolution can be deemed to be scientific (in spite of its brazen contradiction with the scientific evidence), then the Creation model should be considered as a scientific option as well—and the preferred scientific option, since it harmonizes with the scientific evidence.

Eugenie Scott, the Executive Director of the National Center for Science Education, claims that the Creation model is unscientific, since "[t]he ultimate statement of creationism—that the present universe came about as the result of the action or actions of a divine Creator—is thus outside the abilities of science to test" (2004, p. 19). As with Dawkins, however, she also embraces a double-standard on this point. Concerning the gathering of scientific data, she highlighted the importance of indirect observation, stating:

> In some fields, not only is it impossible to directly control the variables, but the phenomena themselves **may not be directly observable**. A research design known as *indirect experimentation* is often utilized in such fields. Explanations can be tested **even if the phenomena being studied are too far away, too small, or too far back in time to be observed directly**. For example, giant planets recently have been

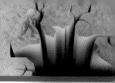
discovered orbiting distant stars—though we cannot directly observe them (2004, p. 6, emp. added, italics in orig.).

She further admitted, "Indeed, no paleontologist has ever observed one species evolving into another, but as we have seen, a theory can be scientific even if its phenomena are not directly observable" (2004, p. 14). Again, may we ask, why is the Creation model deemed "unscientific" today simply because humans did not directly observe Creation, while evolution is deemed "scientific" when, not only have many of its fundamental claims not been directly observed, but the scientific evidence refutes them?

The Universe is saturated with indirect evidence for the existence of God. It has been deemed "scientific" to examine the evidence and conclude that a meteor hit Arizona thousands of years ago, leaving a crater, when allegedly no one was there to witness the occurrence ("Meteor Crater...," 2013). Why is it **not** scientific to conclude from an abundance of scientific evidence that design in the Universe demands a Designer, the laws of science require a law Writer, the effect of the Universe demands a Cause, the Laws of Thermodynamics demand an external creative Source, and the existence of life, information, and its various kinds demand a supernatural Creator? Rather than defining "science" as using observation and experiment to determine the **natural** explanation of phenomena, why not define it as using observation and experiment to determine the **actual** explanation of phenomena—whether natural or not?

In 2011, cosmologist George F.R. Ellis of the University of Cape Town, co-author with Stephen Hawking of the book *The Large Scale Structure of Space-Time*, wrote an article titled, "Does the Multiverse Really Exist?" Speaking of the process by which many cosmologists, including himself, have accepted the multiverse theory (i.e., the idea that there are multiple "universes," rather than the one in which we reside), he said, "The key step in justifying a multiverse is extrapolation from the known to the unknown [i.e., from what can be known through observation to what we cannot observe—JM], from the testable to the untestable" (2011, p. 43). Many scientists are willing to make a leap in accepting things that they cannot observe or test—thus contradicting themselves in their accusations against theists—even when their conclusions are highly speculative and without conclusive evidence, as in the case of the multiverse. Christians, on the other hand, not only can provide solid philosophical arguments for the existence of God, supported by scientific observation, as well as point out clear examples of intelligent design in the Universe which require a Designer, but they can provide a Book which reasonably proves itself to be above the writing capability of human beings.

Bottom line: if evolution is true, science should support it. If Creation is true, science should support it. Why would science lie? It has no agenda. It has no bias. Sadly, many individuals do (scientists included), but why would science? One should not have to continually adjust and jump through hoops to maintain a belief, if it is **the truth**. The question one must be willing to ask himself is, "Which model harmonizes better with the evidence, regardless of my personal wishes?" Only then can one claim to be unprejudiced and sincerely interested in the pursuit of truth. British physicist H.S. Lipson admitted that Creation, not evolution, is the "only acceptable explanation" in keeping with the evidence. "I know that this is anathema to physicists, as indeed it is to me, but we must not reject a theory that we do not like if the experimental evidence supports it" (1980, 31:138).

Science supports the Creation model and not the evolutionary model. Consider: biblical creationists do not have to constantly revise their model to stay in line with science. The creationist platform is in perfect harmony with the laws of science—a circumstance that should characterize any platform that is true. On the other hand, recalling the words of Hoyle and Wickramasinghe, one should "be **suspicious** of a theory if **more and more hypotheses** are needed to support it as new facts become available, or as new considerations are brought to bear" (1981, p. 135, emp. added). That statement does not characterize the Creation model. In the words of Blair Scott of American Atheists, Inc., "The theological arguments have not changed much over [thousands of—JM]...years" (Butt and Scott, 2011). However, it is clear as one considers the history of evolutionary theories, that evolutionists must constantly adapt old theories and develop new

theories to try to postpone the inevitable: the eventual collapse of naturalistic theories. The theories and hypotheses they propose have no basis in solid, conclusive science. They are simply frantic attempts to prop up a failed theory while creating the illusion that it has scientific substance and will "**one day**" be verified.

But notice carefully that each time the new, revised theory is shown to be false and collapses under the weight of truth, the laws of science are still standing—unscathed—as a beacon to those who are sincerely interested in finding the truth. Atheistic evolution—naturalism—does not bear up under scientific scrutiny. The laws of science stand as testimonies against it, and the attempts to respond to the laws simply do not pass the test. In the words of Philip Yam, writing in the popular science journal *Scientific American*, "Certainly, there should be room for far-out, potentially revolutionary ideas, **but not at the expense of solid science**" (1997, p. 85, emp. added). Although he was not directly speaking about naturalistic evolution, his statement perfectly fits in this discussion. What can be considered more "solid science" than the laws of science? And what theory comes more into conflict with solid science than atheistic evolution? Since an examination of the evidence leaves atheism as an implausible idea, that necessitates theism as the rational choice.

In his book, *The Symbiotic Universe*, astronomer George Greenstein of Amherst College said, "As we survey all the evidence, the thought insistently arises that some supernatural agency—or, rather, Agency—must be involved. Is it possible that suddenly, without intending to, we have stumbled upon scientific proof of the existence of a Supreme Being? Was it God who stepped in and so providentially crafted the cosmos for our benefit?" (1988, p. 27). Although Greenstein went on to reject that option, as do many due to their biases against God, more and more naturalistic scientists are openly acknowledging the fact that they keep running into God in their studies. Sadly, they then proceed to sidestep Him and continue along their irrational, Godless path.

Recall the famous astronomer Robert Jastrow. In his book, *God and the Astronomers*, he said, "For the scientist who has lived by his faith in the power of reason, the story ends like a bad dream. He has scaled the mountains of ignorance; he is about to conquer the highest peak; as he pulls himself over the final rock, he is greeted by a band of theologians who have been sitting there for centuries" (1978, p. 116). Science points to God. By all means, use science and observation to make a judgment about Him. As has been shown in this book, the same science that repudiates evolution supports the true Creation model. It always has.

Conclusion

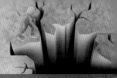

Common Quibbles

- "Unlike Evolutionists, Creationists Have a Blind, Evidence-less Faith!" [See Appendix 6.e]
- "Why are You Even Fighting Evolution, Anyway? Why would it Hurt the Creationist to Just Believe it?" [See Appendix 6.f]
- "Even if There is a God, How Do You Know He's the God of the Bible?" [See Appendix 6.g]

Review Questions

1) What are the five fundamental planks of cosmic evolution that are disproved by the scientific evidence discussed in this book?
2) What faulty assumption undergirds today's definition of "science"?
3) What will be the case if a proposition is true?
4) Articulate a better definition of "science" than that which is used by naturalists today?

APOLOGETICS PRESS, INC.
230 Landmark Drive
Montgomery, AL 36117

JEFF MILLER, Ph.D.
Science Department

Phone:	(334) 272-8558
Phone Orders:	(800) 234-8558
Web Site:	www.apologeticspress.org
E-mail:	jeff@apologeticspress.org

A Non-Profit, Tax-Exempt Work Dedicated to the Defense of New Testament Christianity

Hey, Loret:

Finally finished up a book I've been working on for years, (at least in my mind). Thought you guys might enjoy an early copy. ☺

—Jeff

P.S. I also enclosed a book I finished reading recently. It may change your life.

Common Quibbles with Creationist Arguments

Introduction

How does the evolutionist respond to the arguments presented in the previous chapters? In this part of the book, we wish to respond to what we believe to be the evolutionary community's typical responses to those arguments.

Quibbles with the Laws of Science

Appendix 1.a

"You Creationists Scoff at Theories as Though They are Simply Reckless, Uneducated Guesses."

Don't "Throw the Baby Out with the Bathwater": Not All Theories are Bad!

Perhaps you have fallen victim to the fallacy alluded to by the title of this appendix. Creationists spend quite a bit of time countering the claims being made by those who believe in the theory of evolution and the Big Bang Theory—and rightly so. However, in our haste to show the flaws in evolutionary theories that contradict the laws of science, the impression might be left that we believe scientific theories are somehow unimportant, or are to be rejected and even scoffed at, simply because they are theories. Let's set the record straight.

According to the *McGraw-Hill Dictionary of Scientific and Technical Terms,* a scientific theory is "an attempt to explain a certain class of phenomena" by deducing them from other known principles (p. 2129). Scientific theories are crucial and very beneficial to the work of a scientist. They are a starting place to try to explain and make sense of scientific evidence that has been gathered. Much of what we know to be true in science started out as theory that was later verified or proved and re-categorized.

In biblical apologetics, "theories" are often proposed concerning the meaning of a certain difficult text. For example, in Matthew 20:29-34

137

and Mark 10:46-52, the Bible records an incident where Jesus is said to have been **leaving** Jericho, and seemingly the same incident is recorded in Luke 18:35-43, where it says that the event happened while Jesus was **drawing near** to Jericho. Mark and Luke say that **one** blind man was healed in this incident, while Matthew says that **two** blind men were healed. Eric Lyons discussed various "theories" which adequately explain what is likely happening in these passages (e.g., there were two Jerichos in the first century—the Old Testament Jericho, a small village in the first century, and the Herodian Jericho, two miles southwest)—reasonable theories which illustrate that the Bible in no way contradicts itself (Lyons, 2004). While many of these theories may not ever be known as "gospel" this side of eternity, those theories should not be considered "bad" or things to be scoffed at. Creation scientists also suggest "theories" in order to attempt to explain various scientific observations in light of biblical revelation (e.g., the Flood or the Creation account).

Theories can be good—as long as they are accepted for what they are. A theory looks at the evidence and attempts to explain what **may** be going on—but it does not necessarily yield **definites**. Werner Gitt, retired director of the Information Technology Division at the German Federal Institute of Physics and Technology, explained that a theory is "a scientific statement based on empirical findings. **Since empirical results are seldom final, theories are of a provisional nature**, and the inherent hypothetical element inevitably causes uncertainty—in the best case, a statement can be made in terms of specific probabilities" (2007, Ch. 2, emp. added). Theories are "maybes." That is why there can be multiple theories to try to explain the same observed phenomena, and yet those theories can be totally different from each other and can even contradict one another without, at the same time, contradicting the evidence. One scientist says, "Well, I believe **this** is what's going on." Another scientist says, "Well, maybe, but I think **this** explains that phenomena better"; or "Yes, I agree, but I also think **this** is going on." They have both proposed theories, and may find out in time that they are both right, only one of them is right, or neither is right. But for the moment, their explanations are

merely theories—possible explanations of what they are witnessing. A theory may ultimately be proven wrong in the long run, and if not, it will still likely be revised to some extent.

Scientific Theories and Scientific Evidence

That said, a fundamental rule for developing a scientific theory is that the theory must be in keeping with the scientific evidence—not in contradiction to it. A law of science trumps a "theory" if the two contradict one another, because a law, by definition, is known with certainty to describe nature and is considered to be without exception—beyond doubt. For example, if John Smith proposes a "theory" that claims that a "perpetual motion machine" could be made by combining certain mechanical components in a certain way, he would likely be scoffed at by the engineering community, since the Laws of Thermodynamics forbid the design of such a machine (see Appendix 1.b). The laws of science trump theories that contradict them.

Theories are not, in and of themselves, bad. In fact, they are very good for science. The key is to develop theories that are in keeping with the evidence, and reject those theories that are found to be in contradiction to it. As has been explained, cosmic evolution contradicts the laws of science in many ways, and yet many in the scientific community blindly cling to the Big Bang Theory and Darwinian evolution when those theories should be rejected. We should be sure not to "throw the baby out with the bathwater" with regard to the importance of scientific theory, but if the bathwater needs to be thrown out, do it, or you could hurt the baby—the progress of science.

Review Questions

1) What is a scientific theory?
2) What are some examples of theories that are proposed by creationists?
3) Though theories can be good, what do they not yield?

Appendix 1.b

"Couldn't There Have Been (or Be) Exceptions to the Laws of Science?"

Some have realized the implications of the laws of science concerning the matter of origins. Simply put, the laws of science contradict the atheistic evolutionary model in several places. So, the question is asked by both sincere and unrelinquishing people, "Could there not have been exceptions at some time in the past to the laws of science? Could there not be exceptions in the future?"

Recall that the *McGraw-Hill Dictionary of Scientific and Technical Terms* defines a scientific law as, "a regularity which applies to **all** members of a broad class of phenomena" (2003, p. 1182, emp. added). Not **some**. In other words, all available evidence indicates that the law has always and will always hold true. As long as the scientist takes care to make sure that the law applies to the scenario in question, the evidence indicates that the law will always hold true. According to its definition, a scientific law has no known exceptions, or else it would not be a law in the first place. Stephen Hawking, in his book *The Grand Design*, said concerning the laws of nature, "These laws should hold **everywhere and at all times**; otherwise they wouldn't be laws. There could be **no exceptions**" (2010, p. 171, emp. added). A "theory," on the other hand, is an "attempt to explain" phenomena by deduction from other known principles (*McGraw-Hill...*, p. 2129). A theory may not be true, but a law, by definition, is **always**, and has **always** been, true. Since there are no known exceptions to scientific laws, would it not be unscientific for evolutionists to assert, without any scientific evidence, that there have been exceptions to the laws of science in the past?

Consider again, the Laws of Thermodynamics. A perpetual-motion machine is a device that attempts to violate either the First or Second Law of Thermodynamics (Cengel and Boles, 2002, p. 263). Numerous attempts have been made over the years to design such a machine—all to no avail. However, a prominent thermodynamics textbook used in mechanical engineering schools says concerning such attempts, "The proposers of perpetual-motion machines generally have innovative minds, but they usually lack formal engineering training" (Cengel and Boles, p. 265). Why would the writers make such a statement? The answer is that the Laws of Thermodynamics, which are taught in-depth in mechanical engineering curricula, prohibit the design of such a machine. According to the textbook writers, to spend time and energy on such a pursuit categorizes the pursuer as unknowledgeable about such scientific truths.

The Laws of Thermodynamics have been substantiated to the point that in 1918 the U.S. Patent Office declared that they would no longer accept patent applications for alleged perpetual-motion machines (Cengel and Boles, p. 265). Concerning patent application rejections, the U.S. Patent and Trademark Office Web site says, "a rejection on the ground of lack of utility...can include the more specific grounds of inoperativeness, such as inventions involving **perpetual motion**" (United States Patent..., 2008, emp. added). The Laws of Thermodynamics do not have exceptions. No wonder Borgnakke and Sonntag articulate in *Fundamentals of Thermodynamics* concerning the First and Second Laws of Thermodynamics:

> The basis of every law of nature is experimental evidence, and this is true also of the first law of thermodynamics. Many different experiments have been conducted on the first law, and **every one** [i.e., not most—JM] thus far has verified it either directly or indirectly. The first law has **never been disproved**.... [W]e can say that the second law of thermodynamics (**like every other law of nature**) rests on experimental evidence. **Every relevant experiment** that has been conducted, either directly or indirectly, verifies the second law, and **no experiment has ever been conducted that contradicts the second law**. The basis of

the second law is therefore experimental evidence (Borgnakke and Sonntag, 2009, pp. 116-220, emp. added, parenthetical item in orig.).

Cengel, Turner, and Cimbala affirm this truth in *Fundamentals of Thermal-Fluid Sciences*, saying, "To date, **no experiment** has been conducted that contradicts the second law, and this should be taken as sufficient proof of its validity" (2008, p. 266, emp. added). As far as science can tell, its laws have never been violated. They are without exception. Stephen Hawking said:

> But what's really important is that these physical laws, as well as being **unchangeable**, are universal. They apply not just to the flight of the ball, but to the motion of a planet and everything else in the Universe. Unlike laws made by humans, **the laws of nature cannot ever be broken**. That's why they are so powerful.... [T]he laws of nature are **fixed** ("Curiosity...," 2011, emp. added).

Is it possible that scientists have mis-defined a scientific phenomenon as a law, when it should not have been designated a law in the first place? In other words, could it be that there are unknown circumstances or further future observations that could lead to the violation of a law of science in the future, stripping it of its status as a law? Certainly. Any priniciple that has been designated a law without adequate evidence could potentially be refuted in the future (e.g., Haeckel's Biogenetic Law). Some scientific laws are considered lower in scientific status (e.g., those with less observational and convergent evidence to substantiate them) than others. Obviously, we humans are not omniscient nor omnipresent and could not possibly have the ability to observe nor understand every possible set of relevant circumstances that could ever be. Some principles are, therefore, held as more suspect than others for years while more observations and experiments are made.

Some laws, however, are established as true beyond doubt due to years of investigation and hundreds of validating experiments. The evidence that has been gathered in support of those laws is **extensive and decisive**. Some are even deemed "superlaws"—laws about laws (e.g., the Law of Biogenesis) that carry "the highest rank" in their "levels of organization" (Moore and Slusher, 1974, p. 74). The Laws of Thermodynamics would hardly fall into the category of laws that could be suspected of being erroneous. That is why Cengel and Boles stated that the Laws of Thermodynamics "have been in existence since the creation of the universe" (p. 2). The First Law of Thermodynamics is said to be "the single most important and fundamental 'law of nature' presently known to science, and is one of the most firmly established" (Young, 1985, p.165). It is described as "a firmly established scientific fact" (Jastrow, 1977, p. 32). The Laws of Thermodynamics are not said to be "merely general tendencies or possibly only theoretical considerations," but rather, are "hard as nails" (Walters, 1986, 9[2]:8). The Second Law of Thermodynamics is described as "the ruling paradigm" of the modern period of history, "the premier law of all science," and the "supreme metaphysical law of the entire universe" (Rifkin, 1980, p. 6). These are hardly descriptions that warrant the Laws of Thermodynamics being suspected of having unknown exceptions.

Further, ultimately, "could they be violated?" is not the important question to ask. It is not that there **could** be unknown exceptions to a law. It is that all the evidence says that there **are none**—and science is said to stand with the **evidence**—with what has been observed to be the case. To develop a theory that **requires** the violation of a well-esteemed law when there is no evidence that such could happen is, by definition, **irrational**. Such a step would be tantamount to a pointless hope in an evidence-less position—a genuine blind faith. From a scientific perspective, the evolutionary model falls short of being able to account for the origin of the Universe. Indeed, it contradicts the well-known, highly revered laws of science that govern the Universe. The Creation model, on the other hand, is in perfect harmony with the laws of science.

Review Questions

1) What is the definition of a law of science?

2) Can a law of science have exceptions?

3) What is a "perpetual motion machine," and how does it apply to the discussion of "exceptions" to the laws?

4) Why is it irrational to postulate that the laws of science could be or have been violated?

Quibbles with the Laws of Thermodynamics

"Doesn't Quantum Mechanics Prove That the Universe Could Come From Nothing?"

According to the First Law of Thermodynamics, nothing in the Universe (i.e., matter or energy) can pop into existence from nothing (see chapter two). **All** of the scientific evidence points to that conclusion. So, the Universe could not have popped into existence before the alleged "big bang" (an event which we do not endorse). Therefore, God must have created the Universe.

One of the popular recent rebuttals by the atheistic community is that quantum mechanics could have created the Universe. In 1905, Albert Einstein proposed the idea of mass-energy equivalence, resulting in the famous equation, $E = mc^2$ (1905). We now know that matter can be converted to energy, and vice versa. However, energy and mass are conserved, in keeping with the First Law of Thermodynamics. In the words of the famous evolutionary astronomer, Robert Jastrow, "[T]he principle of the conservation of matter and energy...states that matter and energy can be neither created nor destroyed. Matter can be converted into energy, and vice versa, but the total amount of all matter and energy in the Universe must remain unchanged forever" (1977, p. 32). The idea of matter-energy conversion led one physicist to postulate, in essence, that the cosmic egg that allegedly exploded billions of years ago in the alleged Big Bang—commencing the "creation" of the Universe—could have come into existence as an energy-to-matter conversion.

In 1973, physicist Edward Tryon of the Hunter College of the City University of New York published a paper in the British science journal

Science vs. Evolution

Nature titled, "Is the Universe a Vacuum Fluctuation?" He proposed the idea that the Universe could be a large scale vacuum energy fluctuation. He said, "In answer to the question of **why** it happened, I offer the modest proposal that our universe is simply one of those things which happen from time to time" (246:397, emp. added). Does it really? Cosmologist and theoretical physicist Alexander Vilenkin, Director of the Institute of Cosmology at Tufts University, said:

> Now, what Tryon was suggesting was that our entire universe, with its vast amount of matter, was a huge quantum fluctuation, which somehow failed to disappear for more than 10 billion years. Everybody thought that was a very funny joke. But Tryon was not joking. He was devastated by the reaction of his colleagues... (2006, p. 184).

Though he was originally scoffed at, Tryon's theory has gained traction among many prominent evolutionary scientists. After all, if true, according to Vilenkin, "such a creation event would not require a cause" for the Universe (pp. 184-185).

Speculation vs. Observation

The fact is, the idea that such an event could happen is pure speculation and conjecture. No such phenomenon—the conversion from energy to matter of an entire Universe—has ever been remotely observed. It is a desperate attempt to hold to naturalistic presuppositions, in spite of the evidence, when a supernatural option that is in keeping with the evidence is staring us in the face. Evolutionary physicist Victor Stenger said,

> [T]he universe is probably the result of a random quantum fluctuation in a spaceless, timeless void.... So what had to happen to start the universe was the formation of an empty bubble of highly curved space-time. How did this bubble form? What *caused* it? Not everything requires a cause. It could have just happened spontaneously as one of the many linear combinations of universes that has the quantum numbers of the void.... **Much is still in the speculative stage,** and I must admit that there are yet **no empirical or observational tests that can be used to test the idea of an accidental origin** (1987, 7[3]:26-30, italics in orig., emp. added.).

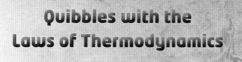

No evidence. No scientific observation. Just speculation. And what's more, according to Stenger's own evolutionary community, if science fundamentally involves "recognizing the **causes** and effects of [material—JM] phenomena"; and if "progress in science consists of the development of better explanations for the **causes** of natural phenomena"; then a causeless material Universe is fundamentally unscientific (Teaching about Evolution..., 1998, p. 42, emp. added). And further, according to the National Academy of Sciences, postulating such a theory will not lead to "progress in science."

No wonder Ralph Estling, writing in the *Skeptical Inquirer* in 1994, voiced strong disapproval of the idea that the Universe could create itself out of nothing. He wrote:

> I do not think that what these cosmologists, these quantum theorists, these universe-makers, are doing is **science**. I can't help feeling that universes are **notoriously disinclined** to spring into being, ready-made, out of nothing, even if Edward Tryon (ah, a name at last!) has written that "our universe is simply one of those things which happen from time to time...." **Perhaps, although we have the word of many famous scientists for it, our universe is not simply one of those things that happen from time to time** (18[4]:430, parenthetical item in orig., emp. added).

Estling's comments initiated a wave of controversy and letters to the *Skeptical Inquirer*, eliciting a response by Estling to his critics. Among other observations, he said, "**All things begin with speculation, science not excluded**. But if no **empirical evidence** is eventually forthcoming, or can be forthcoming, all speculation is barren.... **There is no evidence**, so far, that the entire universe, observable and unobservable, emerged from a state of absolute Nothingness" (1995, 19[1]:69-70, emp. added). Therefore, by naturalists' own definition of science, such an idea is **unscientific**. There is no evidence that could prove such a thing. The creationist platform is in keeping with observational science and has positive evidence of a divine Being from, for example, the presence of intelligent design in nature, the existence of objective morality, the existence of a Universe which demands a cause, and the existence of a Book that contains supernatural characteristics.

However, unlike the creationist platform, those who believe in Tryon's theory are holding to a blind, irrational faith.

From Whence Came Energy?

Consider also, even if such a thing were possible—that energy could be converted to matter in the way that Tryon has suggested—one must ask, "Where did the energy come from?" Alan Guth, professor

of physics at M.I.T., wrote in response to Tryon: "In this context, a proposal that the universe was created from empty space is no more fundamental than a proposal that the universe was spawned by a piece of rubber. It might be true, but one would still want to ask **where the piece of rubber came from**" (1997, p. 273, emp. added).

Energy could not have popped into existence without violating the First Law Thermodynamics (i.e., the Law of Conservation of Mass/Energy). Prominent atheistic writer David Mills, in his book, *Atheist Universe*, wrote, "Many people, including some atheists and agnostics, misinterpret Big Bang theory as proposing that mass-energy popped into existence ex nihilo [i.e. out of nothing] before the universe began its current expansion. This something-from-nothing belief is not only false, but flagrantly violates the law of conservation of mass-energy" (2006, p. 30, bracketed comment in orig.). So in reality, when scientists argue that quantum mechanics creates something from nothing, they do not really mean "nothing." The problem of how everything got here is still present.

The matter generated in quantum theory is from a vacuum **that is not void**. Philip Yam of *Scientific American* admitted, "Energy in the vacuum, though, is very much real. According to modern physics, **a vacuum isn't a pocket of nothingness**. It churns with unseen activity even at absolute zero, the temperature defined as the point at which all molecular motion ceases" (1997, p. 82, emp. added). Prominent humanist mathematician and science writer, Martin Gardner, wrote:

"It is fashionable now to conjecture that the big bang was caused by a random quantum fluctuation in a vacuum devoid of space and time. But of course such a vacuum is **a far cry from nothing**" (2000, p. 303, emp. added). Amanda Gefter, writing in *New Scientist*, said, "Quantum mechanics tells us that **the vacuum of space is not empty**; instead, it crackles with energy" (2010, p. 29, emp. added). Physicist Richard Morris agreed:

> In modern physics, **there is no such thing as "nothing."** Even in a perfect vacuum, pairs of virtual particles are constantly being created and destroyed [i.e., formed by briefly "borrowing" energy already in existence and then returning it—JM]. The existence of these particles is no mathematical fiction. Though they cannot be directly observed, the effects they create are quite real. The assumption that they exist leads to predictions that have been confirmed by experiment to a high degree of accuracy (1990, p. 25, emp. added).

Astrophysicist Rocky Kolb, chairman of the Department of Astronomy and Astrophysics at the University of Chicago, wrote: "[A] region of seemingly empty space is **not really empty**, but is a seething froth in which every sort of fundamental particle pops in and out of empty space before annihilating with its antiparticle and disappearing" (1998, 26[2]:43, emp. added). Estling continued his extensive observations in response to his critics (mentioned above), saying:

> Quantum cosmologists insist both on this absolute Nothingness and on endowing it with various qualities and characteristics: this partic-ular Nothingness possesses virtual quanta seething in a false vacuum. **Quanta, virtual or actual, false or true, are not Nothing, they are definitely Something**, although we may argue over what exactly. For one thing, quanta are entities **having energy**, a vacuum has energy and moreover, extension, i.e., it is something into which other things, such as universes, can be put, i.e., **we cannot have our absolute Nothingness and eat it too**. If we have quanta and a vacuum as given, we in fact have a pre-existent state of existence that either pre-existed timelessly or brought itself into existence from absolute Nothingness (no quanta, no vacuum, no pre-existing initial conditions) at some precise moment in time; it creates this time, along with the space, matter, and energy, which we call the universe.... I've had correspondence with Paul Davies

[who advocates the supposition that the Universe created itself from nothing—JM] on cosmological theory, in the course of which, I asked him what he meant by "Nothing." He wrote back that he had asked Alexander Vilenkin what he meant by it and that Vilenkin had replied, "By Nothing I mean Nothing," which seemed pretty straightforward at the time, but **these quantum cosmologists go on from there to tell us what their particular breed of Nothing consists of**. I pointed this out to Davies, who replied that these things are very complicated. I'm willing to admit the truth of that statement, **but I think it does not solve the problem** (1995, 19[1]:69-70, emp. added).

No wonder Jonathan Sarfati said:

Some physicists assert that quantum mechanics...can produce something from nothing.... But this is a gross misapplication of quantum mechanics. **Quantum mechanics never produces something out of nothing**.... Theories that the Universe is a quantum fluctuation must presuppose that **there was something to fluctuate**—their "quantum vacuum" is a lot of matter-antimatter potential—not "nothing" (1998, 12[1]:21, emp. added).

Vilenkin, while explaining the problems inherent in Tryon's work, said:

A more fundamental problem is that Tryon's scenario does not really explain the origin of the universe. A quantum fluctuation of the vacuum assumes that there was a vacuum of some pre-existing space. And we now know that **"vacuum" is very different from "nothing."** Vacuum, or empty space, **has energy and tension**, it can bend and warp, so it is unquestionably *something* (2006, p. 185, italics in orig., emp. added).

He went on to propose that quantum tunneling could be the answer to the creation of the Universe out of nothing. However, quantum tunneling starts with **something** and ends with **something** as well. Particles that can jump or tunnel through barriers still must initially exist to do so. Bottom line: according to Stephen Hawking, in order to create a Universe, "**you need** just three ingredients": matter, energy, and space ("Curiosity...," 2011, emp. added). Those three ingredients must exist in order to create a Universe, according to Hawking. **So, the problem remains. Where did the ingredients for the Universe soup come from? There must be an ultimate Cause of the Universe.**

Non-Existent Quantum Law-Maker?

Third, even if one were to irrationally accept the premise that quantum theory allows for the possibility that Universes could pop into existence, in the words of astrophysicist Marcus Chown:

> If the universe owes its origins to quantum theory, then quantum theory must have existed before the universe. So the next question is surely: **where did the laws of quantum theory come from**? "We do not know," admits Vilenkin. "I consider that an entirely different question." When it comes to the beginning of the universe, in many ways we're still at the beginning (2012, p. 35, emp. added).

Martin Gardner said:

> Imagine that physicists finally discover all the basic waves and their particles, and all the basic laws, and unite everything in one equation. We can then ask, "Why that equation?" It is fashionable now to conjecture that the big bang was caused by a random quantum fluctuation in a vacuum devoid of space and time. But of course such a vacuum is a far cry from nothing. **There had to be quantum laws to fluctuate. And why are there quantum laws?**... **There is no escape from the superultimate questions: Why is there something rather than nothing, and why is the something structured the way it is?** (2000, p. 303, emp. added).

In "Curiosity: Did God Create the Universe?" Stephen Hawking boldly claimed that everything in the Universe can be accounted for through atheistic evolution without the need of God. This is untrue, as we have discussed in earlier chapters (cf. Miller, 2011a), but it seems that Hawking does not even believe that assertion himself. He asked the question, "**Did God create the quantum laws** that allowed the Big Bang to occur? In a nutshell, did we need a god to set it all up so that the Big Bang could bang?" ("Curiosity...," emp. added). He then proceeded to offer no answer to the question. In his critique of Hawking, Paul Davies highlighted this very fact, saying, "You need to know where those laws come from. That's where the mystery lies—the laws" ("The Creation Question...," 2011). Quantum mechanics, with its governing laws, simply does not leave room for the spontaneous generation of universes.

Responses

But what if quantum theory could allow for spontaneous generation at the quantum level? What if the First Law of Thermodynamics does not apply at the unobservable molecular world of quantum mechanics but only to the macroscopic world that we can actually see? Even if that were the case (and there is no conclusive evidence to support the contention that there are **any exceptions** whatsoever to the First Law of Thermodynamics—see Appendix 1.b), according to the Big Bang model, the **quantum level** cosmic egg eventually became **macroscopic** through expansion or inflation. Such an event would have been the equivalent of a breach of the First Law, even under such a speculative definition.

But isn't it true that, as Andrei Linde, cosmologist and professor of physics at Stanford University, wrote, "one usually assumes that the current laws of physics did not apply" at the beginning (1994)? If the laws of physics broke down at the beginning, one cannot use quantum law to bring about matter, which is precisely what the quantum fluctuation theory attempts to do. [NOTE: See Appendix 2.c for a discussion of this topic].

But if gravity is negative energy and matter is positive energy, doesn't the total energy of the Universe equal zero? So, the First Law wouldn't be violated if the Universe started with no energy before the Big Bang and ended with a sum total zero energy after, right? The First Law of Thermodynamics prohibits the creation of energy. Regardless of the sum total, if one starts with zero energy and ends with both positive and negative energy, energy has been created. [NOTE: See Appendix 2.b for more on this topic.]

Conclusion

Can quantum mechanics create Universes from **nothing**? No. Quantum particle generation requires pre-existing energy—a far cry from nothing. Could quantum mechanics spontaneously create Universes from pre-existing energy (energy which would have to originate from God)? There is no scientific evidence to support such a proposition. So it is speculation and conjecture—wishful thinking on par with postulating that aliens brought life to Earth, which some irrationally believe (see Appendix 4.c). Tiny quantum particles fluctuating—bouncing around—is one thing. The creation of the entire Universe through a quantum fluctuation? That's another.

One who wishes to avoid acknowledging the existence of God should be expected to do almost anything to deny it. In the words of Scottish philosopher David Hume, "No man turns against reason until reason turns against him" (as quoted in Warren, 1982, p. 4). Reason will be thrown aside, and acceptance of far-fetched theories—theories that are so speculative that they belong in the fiction section of the library along with the *The Wizard of Oz*—will be latched onto as fact. The Bible gives the rationale for this irrational behavior by explaining that such a person has "itching ears" (2 Timothy 4:3). Such a person will "heap up...teachers" that will tell him what he wants to hear, who sound smart, and therefore, will make him feel good about the blatantly irrational position to which he clings (vs. 3). He will turn his "ears away from the truth, and be turned aside to fables" (vs. 4). Thus, "professing themselves to be wise, they became fools" (Romans 1:22). The quantum fluctuation idea is simply another example of this same mentality, and the admonition to Christians is the same as it was in the first century: "But you be watchful in all things" (vs. 5). "Guard what was committed to your trust, avoiding the profane and idle babblings and contradictions of what is falsely called knowledge" (1 Timothy 6:20).

Review Questions

1) What is the basic argument that Edward Tryon made concerning the Universe?

2) Since there is no evidence for the spontaneous generation of Universes, what can theories that propose such things be said to be?

3) Even if the Universe could pop into existence through quantum fluctuations, what would the atheist still need to explain the origin of?

4) Even if one could explain the origin of matter and energy, what must the atheist still explain the origin of?

5) What are some rebuttals a person might have to the line of reasoning proposed in this chapter, and what would be the responses?

"The Zero Energy Balance in the Universe Allowed it to Pop into Existence."

Perhaps it seems like common sense to you that universes do not create themselves—popping into existence all over the place, but many naturalistic scientists are latching on to such bizarre ideas due to their lack of a naturalistic explanation for the origin of the Universe. Stephen Hawking said, "Bodies such as stars or black holes cannot just appear out of nothing. But **a whole universe can**.... Because there is a law like gravity, **the universe can and will create itself from nothing**" (2010, p. 180, emp. added). Is there any empirical evidence suggesting that universes can pop into existence? Absolutely not. Is there evidence that **anything** can pop into existence from nothing? Nope. We have a law of science that prohibits it—the First Law of Thermodynamics (see chapter two). Does the idea that something could pop into existence from nothing remind you of a magician's trick? Probably. But to many in the scientific community today, naturalism **must** be true. They **will not** consider God (Romans 1:18-32). He is not allowed in the discussion. "Creation is unacceptable, but witchcraft? Now **that**...we'll consider."

The Problem for the Naturalist

According to the First Law of Thermodynamics, "energy can be neither created nor destroyed; it can only change forms" (Cengel and Boles, 2002, p. 166). This poses a problem for the atheist, since

Science vs. Evolution

the energy and matter of the Universe had to come from somewhere. Hawking said:

> The idea of inflation could also explain why there is so much matter in the universe. There are something like ten million million million million million million million million million million million million million million million (1 with eighty zeros after it) particles in the region of the universe that we can observe. Where did they all come from? The answer is that, in quantum theory, particles can be created out of energy in the form of particle/antiparticle pairs. But that just raises the question of **where the energy came from** (1988, p. 129, emp. added, parenthetical item in orig.).

In his book, *God: The Failed Hypothesis*, evolutionary physicist Victor Stenger said:

> [W]here does the energy come from? The law of conservation of energy, also known as the *first law of thermodynamics,* requires that energy come from somewhere. In principle, **the creation hypothesis could be confirmed** by the direct observation or theoretical requirement that conservation of energy was violated 13.7 billion years ago at the start of the big bang (2007, p. 116, italics in orig., emp. added).

The Naturalist's Response

Hawking believes he has an answer to this problem for the naturalist—one that is in keeping with the First Law of Thermodynamics:

> The answer is that the total energy of the universe is exactly zero. The matter in the universe is made out of positive energy. However, the matter is all attracting itself by gravity.... Thus, in a sense, the gravitational field has negative energy. In the case of a universe that is approximately uniform in space, one can show that this negative gravitational energy exactly cancels the positive energy represented by the matter. So the total energy of the universe is zero (1988, p. 129).

Stenger concurs. According to him, "The first law allows energy to convert from one type to another as long as the total for a closed system remains fixed. Remarkably, the total energy of the universe appears to be zero" (2007, p. 116).

So these physicists assert, in essence, that there would have been zero energy in the Universe before the alleged big bang (a theory which we do not support, cf. Thompson, et al., 2003), and then there would have been zero energy in the Universe after the big bang, since "matter energy" might be considered to be positive and "gravitational energy" might be considered to be negative. According to Hawking and Stenger, these two amounts cancel each other out, leaving zero energy in the Universe—zero energy before the bang, and zero energy after. Voila! A Universe pops into existence. Sound reasonable to you?

The Evidence from Science and Sense

First of all, notice that Hawking boldly proclaims two significant assumptions that cannot even remotely be verified. (1) The Universe must be "approximately uniform in space"; and (2) The "negative gravitational energy **exactly cancels** the positive energy represented by the matter. So the total energy of the universe is zero" (1988, p. 129, emp. added). How, pray tell, could Hawking know such things about this vast and infinitely complex Universe without being omniscient? Not only can he not know such things, but he cannot even **claim** such things with the meager evidence about the entirety of the Universe he has at his disposal. It is quite a leap to hold to such unverified assumptions. It is a blind faith in a proposition that cannot be established scientifically. The rational man's beliefs are based on the evidence—not baseless speculation.

Second, notice that he says, "**in a sense**, the gravitational field has negative energy" (1988, p. 129, emp. added). The words, "in a sense," are significant, because they highlight the fact that gravitational energy is not really inherently "negative." We call it "negative" from a certain viewpoint when we have such a thing as a directional axis to compare its effect with; but, in actuality, gravitational energy is simply energy—regardless of its sign. Hawking, himself, used the term "energy" to describe gravity. Whether or not it is considered "negative" is not the question. The question in light of the First Law is, where did it come from?

Third, this line of reasoning implies that things could and should be popping into existence all around us all the time, as long as those items have enough negative gravitational energy to offset them. Particles, rocks, and infinitely complex Universes should be popping into existence, since such occurrences—according to these physicists—would not violate a natural law. But wait. That does not happen. It has never been observed to occur—not even once. And our common sense verifies that it will not happen. Science does not support such a hypothesis. The hypothesis is **unscientific**.

Fourth, consider: is there energy in the Universe today that would not have been in existence before the supposed big bang? Yes. If I were to ask Hawking and Stenger if energy exists in the Universe today, what do you suppose they would say? To ask is to answer. But the First Law of Thermodynamics prohibits the **creation of energy**. So, the question is not whether the energy balance before and after the alleged big bang is still zero. The important question in light of the First Law is whether or not there is energy in the Universe today that was not there before the alleged big bang. The answer would have to be, "yes." In fact, there are, by Hawking's own admission, "negative" **and** "positive" energies in existence. According to the First Law of Thermodynamics, they could not have created themselves. Therefore, Someone must have created them.

In essence, Hawking and those who hold to his position are playing word games with "zero." It is like the man who holds out an empty fist and asks a child, "What am I holding in my hand?" The child responds, "Nothing." The man continues, "What is stronger than God?" The child responds, "Nothing." The man then concludes, "So, what I'm holding in my hand is stronger than God." In logic, this is known as a "fallacy of equivocation," which the *Collins English Dictionary* defines as "a fallacy based on the use of the same term in different senses, esp. as the middle term of a syllogism, as *the badger lives in the bank, and the bank is in the High Street, so the badger lives in the High Street*" (2003, italics in orig.; cf. Baum, 1975, pp. 477-478). While there is a Universal energy balance of zero in Hawking's model, it does not mean that there is actually zero energy in the Universe. On the contrary, the

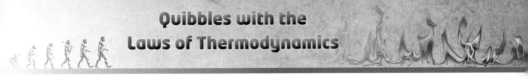
exorbitant amount of energy in the Universe calls for an explanation that can only be given by the Creation model.

Conclusion

In the words of Stenger:

> Conservation of energy [i.e., the First Law of Thermodynamics—JM] and other basic laws **hold true in the most distant observed galaxy** and in the cosmic microwave background, implying that these laws have been valid for over thirteen billion years [NOTE: we do not hold to this deep time supposition—JM]. Surely any observation of their violation during the puny human life span would be reasonably termed a **miracle**.... In principle, **the creation hypothesis could be confirmed** by the direct observation or theoretical requirement that conservation of energy was violated 13.7 billion years ago at the start of the big bang (2007, pp. 115-116, emp. added).

It is truly ironic that Stenger, himself, while attempting to dismiss the necessity of the supernatural in explaining the origin of the Universe, "confirmed" the existence of God through the "theoretical requirement that conservation of energy was violated" in the beginning of time. It is sad that Stenger's admission on this point illustrates that, prior to Hawking's development of this argument, Stenger recognized the need for the supernatural in explaining the origin of energy, since no "scientific" argument was available. Why, sir, did you not accept God before that point? And why, sir, do you not accept Him now, since He alone can account for the existence of the awesome Universe in which we reside? May we suggest that the answer to both questions is the same? Many will not consider God, regardless of the scientific evidence.

Review Questions

1) What problem does the First Law of Thermodynamics pose for the naturalist?

2) What is the response being made by Stephen Hawking and others to this dilemma?

3) What assumptions highlight the speculative nature of Hawking's theory?

4) What is gravity, regardless of its "negative" sign?

5) Since humans have never observed matter or gravity popping into existence, what can truthfully be said of a theory that proposes such an idea?

6) What logical fallacy is Hawking making?

"The Laws of Thermodynamics Didn't Apply in the Beginning."

It is relatively easy for the rational man to disprove the idea that matter can spontaneously generate. Of course, even intuition does not back spontaneous generation. It matters not how long you sit in your chair and stare at an empty desk. A pencil will not eventually materialize on the desk before you. Things—no matter how simplistic—do not pop into existence from nothing.

The idea that **structured, physical law-abiding** matter (i.e., like that which we see all around us in the created order) could come into being from nothing is even more far-fetched. Beyond intuition, this matter is laid to rest when we consider the implications of the First Law of Thermodynamics and the Law of Conservation of Matter (see chapter two). To paraphrase, the amount of energy and matter in a system will remain constant unless there is input from some outside source. In other words, it does not matter how long you stare at the table, unless someone comes by your table and puts an already existing pencil on it, or you put the pencil on it yourself, or it falls on the table from some other place, a pencil will not appear on the table. This idea, applied to the origin of the Universe, indicates that the Universe has either always existed (an idea which violates the Second Law of Thermodynamics—see chapter two) or Someone put it here.

In response, some scientists boldly claim that, concerning the origin of matter, "one usually assumes that the current laws of physics did not apply then" (Linde, 1994). Stephen Hawking stated that in the beginning, at the alleged Big Bang, "the laws of science and our ability to predict the future would break down" (1988, p. 88). Granted—certain assumptions are often necessary in science. Granted—no one was around to make scientific observations about the origin of matter. But wait...that's the point. No one was there. So we have to look at the current evidence to determine what may have happened. But naturalists throw out the current evidence, since it does not provide them with a naturalistic answer to the origin question that they seek, and proceed to engage in wild speculation. How is it scientific to throw aside solid science—making the assumption that there were no such things as laws of science in the beginning—with no evidence to support such a claim? This, naturalists do, even when all empirical evidence that has ever been observed by scientists leads to the conclusion that the laws of physics are, always have been, and always will be immutable (i.e., until they are destroyed along with the physical Universe on the Day of Judgment, 2 Peter 3:7-10)—that they do not "break down." Therefore, if we behave rationally—drawing conclusions based on the evidence—we will conclude that they **did not** "break down."

In fact, evolutionists go through pains to prove the immutability of certain scientific assertions, at least when it suits their agenda. For instance, creationists point out that the dating techniques utilized for evolutionary theory are based on certain assumptions which are far from reasonable—like the assertion that physical constants used in dating methods have remained constant throughout time. Mark Isaak of "The TalkOrigins Archive" attempts to respond to this criticism by describing certain constants which have purportedly remained constant for billions of years (Isaak, 2007). Creationists have no problem with the idea that certain constants could have remained essentially the same over long periods of time (though we do not believe that the Universe has existed for billions of years). However, scientific evidence indicates that not **all** physical constants have remained unchanged forever—specifically constants that are used in evolutionary dating techniques (cf. Stober, 2010; Miller, 2013; Butt, 2010b). For instance, catastrophic events, such as volcanoes (cf. Akahane, et al., 2004), can significantly alter decay rates and the constants involved. The conclusion: dating techniques that make unscientific assumptions

are flawed (cf. Miller, 2013). However, scientific laws, by definition, are without exception.

Notice, however, that naturalistic evolutionists want to "have their cake and eat it, too." On one hand, they do not want to grant that the laws of science have always been constant, although all scientific evidence indicates that they have; but they **do** want to make erroneous claims about physical constants that have been shown to be in contradiction with the scientific evidence since it suits their agenda. Recall that the same Stephen Hawking who claimed that the laws of science would break down at the beginning of the Universe contradicted himself by saying:

> But what's really important is that these physical laws, as well as being **unchangeable**, are **universal**. They apply not just to the flight of the ball, but to the motion of a planet and everything else in the Universe. Unlike laws made by humans, the laws of nature **cannot ever be broken**. That's why they are so powerful.... [T]he laws of nature are **fixed** ("Curiosity...?" 2011, emp. added).

Notice again that the evolutionist's dilemma is not improved upon even if we grant the possibility that the laws of science were inapplicable at the beginning. Would evolutionists have us to believe that in the beginning, not only matter, but the physical laws that govern that matter popped into existence with the matter as well (see chapter one)? How can there be a law without a law maker? How is such an assertion scientific? And how is such an assertion allowed to go unchallenged by many scientists? The bias of those in the evolutionary community against accepting the rational and scientific alternative to their faulty theories is profound.

Further, if the laws of physics broke down at the beginning, one cannot use science—namely quantum law—to bring about matter, which is precisely what naturalists wish to do (see Appendix 2.a). They wish to have a natural explanation for the origin of the Universe that does not require God. **However, if the evolutionist cannot use science and its laws to bring about the Universe, then he has, in reality, given up on naturalism and become a believer in supernaturalism.** In other words, if the laws of nature did not apply in the beginning, by implication, only **supernatural** phenomena could have existed to bring about the Universe. The next step is only to decide which supernatural entity is the true Creator—God, with His supporting evidences, or magic, with its lack thereof. [NOTE: This illustrates that naturalistic theories amount to religion. Consistency would dictate that those schools that do not allow the Creation model to be taught in their science classes should eliminate naturalistic theories as well. However, this author believes that the correct solution would be to teach the evidence from science, wherever it leads. Truth is the goal. The scientific evidence detailed in this book points to a Creator. So it should be taught. Any theory which contradicts the evidence should be removed from scientific discussion. See Houts, 2007 for more on the idea that evolution is religion, not science.]

Although assumptions are often necessary in science, scientific assumptions must carry the quality of being **reasonable** in order for them to be permissible in scientific discussion (cf. Miller, 2013 for a discussion on scientific assumptions). What scientific evidence could be cited to back such a grandiose claim that there was a time that the laws of nature did not hold? The only way the claim that the laws of science did not apply in the beginning can be made and considered to be reasonable is if the person has made another equally unscientific **assumption** upon which that claim is based. The person would have to assume that there was no One here at the beginning that could have organized matter in keeping with the Laws which that Being set in motion. The Creation model in no way contradicts the laws of physics. On the other hand, the atheistic evolutionary model contradicts the laws of physics in a myriad of ways. Yet, creationists are the ones who are branded as unscientific.

Review Questions

1) Is it rational to claim that there was a time when the laws of science did not apply?

2) How are naturalists inconsistent concerning the applicability of the laws of science?

3) What point illustrates the fact that the naturalist is actually a supernaturalist?

"The Universe is Not a Closed System."

The Universe: Not Isolated?

Many in the atheistic community recognize various problems with their theories in light of what we know about the Laws of Thermodynamics. As we have seen, in order for atheism to be a plausible explanation for the origin of the Universe, matter must either be eternal or have the capability of creating itself (i.e., spontaneously generating). Yet the Second Law of Thermodynamics implies that the first option is impossible, and the First Law of Thermodynamics implies that the second option is impossible (see chapter two). Upon grudgingly coming to this conclusion, but being unwilling to yield to the obvious alternative (i.e., Someone outside of the Universe put matter here), some have tried to find loopholes in the Laws that will allow for their flawed atheistic ideologies to survive.

Another assertion being offered today by some is that the Laws of Thermodynamics apply in the Universe, but do not apply to the Universe as a whole, and therefore cannot be used to prove that God played a role in the origin of the Universe. More specifically, some question whether our Universe can be considered an "isolated system" (i.e., a system—like the Universe—in which mass and energy are not allowed to cross the system boundary—i.e., go beyond the material Universe or come into it from another Universe; Cengel and Boles, 2002, p. 9). In their well-known thermodynamics textbook, *Fundamentals of Classical Thermodynamics*, Van Wylen, et. al., though not necessarily naturalists, note concerning the Second Law of Thermodynamics: "[W]e of course do not know if the universe can be considered as an isolated system" (1994, p. 272). Robert Alberty, author of *Thermodynamics of Biochemical Reactions*, is quoted as saying, "I do not agree that the universe is an isolated system in the thermodynamic sense" (as quoted in Holloway, 2010).

What's the Point?

What if the Universe is **not** an isolated system? How would that fact impact the Creation/evolution controversy? First of all, the creationist has always argued that the Universe is **not** an isolated system, or at least has not **always** been one. According to the creationist, in the beginning, God created the Universe's system barrier, then crossed it and placed energy and matter within the system—thus making the Universe non-isolated **in the beginning**. So, evolutionists' recognition that the Universe must not, in fact, be an isolated system would really mean that they are starting to move in the right direction in their understanding of the Universe. It acknowledges the need for a Source external to the Universe. Acquiescence of this truth by atheists in no way disproves the existence of God. In fact, quite the contrary is true. Admission that the Universe is not isolated does not help the case for atheism, but rather tacitly acknowledges a supernatural creator of sorts. [More on this point later.]

What a concession that the Universe could not be an isolated system **would** do, however, is make some of the creationists' arguments against atheism less applicable to the discussion about the existence of God, specifically, some of the uses of the Laws of Thermodynamics and their application to the Universe as a whole. For instance, if the Universe is **not** an isolated system, it means that something (e.g., another Universe or God) exists outside the Universe that can open the proverbial box that encloses the Universe and put matter and energy into it. Therefore, the Universe **could be eternal**, as long as something is putting more usable energy into the box to compensate for the energy loss and counter entropy. Thus, the argument against

the eternality of matter by way of the Second Law of Thermodynamics (discussed in depth in chapter two) would potentially be null and void. But again, such an admission would simultaneously admit that there is something/Someone supernatural (i.e., transcendent of the natural Universe as we know it).

Also, if the Universe was a non-isolated system, it could be argued that the original, imaginary pre-Big Bang ball (which we would argue never actually existed—since the Big Bang Theory has fundamental flaws [see Thompson, et al., 2003]) did not have to be eternal in its existence, since something could have initially created it and put it in the Universe to start the Big Bang process. In other words, it could be contended that it did not have to spontaneously generate in order to explain its existence. So, can the Universe in fact be considered a non-isolated system?

The Universe: Isolated

From a purely scientific perspective, one of the problems with claiming that the Universe is not isolated (and yet God does not exist) is that such an assertion presupposes the existence of physical (i.e., non-spiritual) sources outside of this Universe (e.g., multiple universes outside of our own). And yet, how can such a claim be made, scientifically, since there is no verifiable evidence to support such a contention? Stephen Hawking has advanced such an idea, but he, himself, recognizes the idea to be merely theoretical (Shukman, 2010). Speculation, conjecture, assertion—not evidence. The goal? To explain our existence through any means necessary without having to resort to God. As astrophysicist Gregory Benford of the University of California at Irvine wrote in his book, *What We Believe but Cannot Prove*, "This 'multiverse' view represents the failure of our grand agenda and seems to me contrary to the prescribed simplicity of Occam's Razor, solving our lack of understanding by **multiplying unseen entities into infinity**" (Benford, 2006, p. 226, emp. added). Belief in the multiverse model is like proclaiming the existence of fairies just because you can imagine one. But such speculation is hardly scientific evidence—and that is the problem.

What does the scientific evidence **actually** convey today? We live in the only known material Universe. If the naturalist remains consistent with his definition of science to only include observable, natural phe-

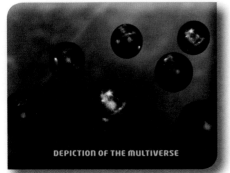

DEPICTION OF THE MULTIVERSE

nomena (i.e., no supernatural Power exists), then he must conclude that the evidence shows the Universe to be an isolated system. That is a fact. If, according to the Law of Rationality, one should only draw those conclusions that can be derived from the evidence (Ruby, 1960, pp. 130-131), the rational man will conclude that only our Universe exists. If the Big Bang occurred, and all matter and energy in the Universe—everything that exists—was initially in that little imaginary sphere the size of the period at the end of this sentence (or much smaller, depending on which cosmologist you ask), by implication, the evolutionist must admit that the Universe is of a **finite size**. That is a fact. A tiny, finite Universe is an isolated system. That isolated system had to come from somewhere.

Since the Universe as a whole is the only **true** isolated system today, the Laws of Thermodynamics apply perfectly. That is why some reputable scientists examine the evidence, draw reasonable conclusions, and articulate statements in prominent textbooks like the following:

- "Isolated system: It is the system which exchange [sic] neither matter nor energy with the surroundings. For such a system, the matter and energy remain constant. There is no such perfectly isolated system, but **our universe can be considered as an isolated system** since by definition it does not have any surroundings" (Senapati, 2006, p. 64, emp. added).

- "*A spontaneous process in an **isolated system** increases the system's entropy*. Because the **universe**—our entire surroundings—**is in contact with no other system**, we say that irreversible processes increase the entropy of the universe" (Fishbane, et.al., 1996, p. 551, italics in orig., emp. added).

There is simply no way around the fact that the laws of science apply to the Universe as a whole. In fact, one physics textbook, used in universities across the nation, called this the *"central dogma* of physics" (Fishbane, et. al, p. 326, italics in orig.). The authors state: "The laws of nature are the same everywhere, be it Cavendish's laboratory, the environs of Earth, the solar system, or extragalactic space" (p. 326). Recall Stephen Hawking's words:

> But what's really important is that these physical laws, as well as being unchangeable, are **universal**. They apply not just to the flight of the ball, but to the motion of a planet and **everything else in the Universe** ("Curiosity...," 2011, emp. added).

The truth is, if one is unwilling to accept the existence of God, yet desires to accept the laws of science, one **must** conjure up other options for how the "Universe box" could have been legally opened and its contents altered. Envision several atheists sitting around a table speculating about options, no matter how wild, in order to avoid conceding the existence of God, and you will have a clear picture of how many in the scientific community operate today. "Okay, people. How did we get here? Think!" "Other universes?" "Maybe." "Nothing put us here?" "Not bad." "Aliens?" "Why not?" "The God of the Bible?" "Shut your mouth. You are unscientific. Leave the room." How can evolutionists like Richard Dawkins and Stephen Hawking safely postulate the existence of alien creators without being laughed out of the spotlight, while creationists get expelled from the scientific community for recogniz-

ing the **reasonable** answer to the matter of origins (Stein and Miller, 2008; "Stephen Hawking Warns...", 2010)?

Implications of the Naturalist's Contention

Ironically, when the atheistic community alleges creative agents outside the Universe, they tacitly acknowledge a creator of some sort. What is the difference between these concessions and the true Creator? Why not accept the God of the Bible? The answer is obvious. Their brand of designer comes packaged without the demands and expectations that come with belief in God: very convenient—but sad and most certainly an irrational, unscientific mentality.

Note also that accepting the possibility of alternative creative causes leaves atheists with the same problem with which they started. They claim to use the laws of physics to arrive at the multiverse conclusion (Shukman, 2010). But if the laws of physics apply to their conclusion about multiple universes, why would the laws of physics not apply **to** those universes? Concerning the multiverse, cosmologist George F.R. Ellis of the University of Cape Town, co-author with Stephen Hawking of the book *The Large Scale Structure of Space-Time*, said, "Each [Universe—JM] has a different initial distribution of matter, but **the same laws of physics operate in all**. Nearly all cosmologists today (including me) [i.e., Ellis, not JM] accept this type of multiverse" (2011, p. 38). If the laws of science apply to those hypothetical universes (and it would be reasonable to conclude that they would since, according to atheists, the universes interact), then the matter of origins has merely shifted to those other universes. How did **they** come into being without God?

Michio Kaku, theoretical physicist of the City College of New York, said, "[I]n string theory, there are other universes out there. There's a multiverse of universes.... And then the question is, 'Where did the multiverse come from?' You could argue, therefore, that maybe you need a god to create the multiverse, or a creator to create string theory, perhaps" ("The Creation Question...," 2011). Paul Davies said, "You still have to explain the multiverse. That still has laws. You need a Universe generating mechanism" ("The Creation Question..."). There are still only three options: (1) They always existed (in violation of the Second Law of Thermodynamics); (2) they created themselves (in violation of the First Law of Thermodynamics); or, (3) as these scientists imply, they were created by a Force outside nature. The Laws of Thermodynamics still echo the truth from the remotest parts of the created order: "You cannot explain it all without God in the equation!"

Conclusion

The truth is, the scientific evidence leads unbiased truth-seekers to the conclusion that there simply must be a Creator. How do we know that the Laws of Thermodynamics are true on Earth? No one has ever been able to document an exception to them (except when divine miracles have occurred). They **always** hold true. Why does the same principle not hold when observing the rest of the Universe? As Borgnakke and Sonntag articulate in *Fundamentals of Thermodynamics* concerning the First and Second Laws of Thermodynamics:

> The basis of every law of nature is experimental evidence, and this is true also of the first law of thermodynamics. Many different experiments have been conducted on the first law, and every one thus far has verified it either directly or indirectly. The first law has never been disproved.... [W]e can say that the second law of thermodynamics (like every other law of nature) rests on experimental evidence. Every relevant experiment that has been conducted, either directly or indirectly, verifies the second law, and **no experiment has ever been conducted that contradicts the second law** (2009, p. 116-220, emp. added, parenthetical item in orig.).

There has been no verifiable evidence that the Laws of Thermodynamics have been violated anywhere throughout the Universe. Sure, there has been speculation, conjecture, and theory that it "could" happen. Yet, through it all, the laws still stand as the only substantiated reality. Granted, atheists may cloud the air when they blow forth their unreasonable, unproven, jargon-filled, imaginary, fairy-dust theories, but when the fairy-dust settles, the Laws of Thermodynamics still declare the truth to all who will listen (Psalm 19:1). The scientific evidence shows that there is unmistakable order and design in the Universe. Design implies a Designer. Now **that's** scientific.

Science vs. Evolution

Review Questions

1) What is an "isolated system"?
2) If the Universe is not "isolated," how would it affect the creationist?
3) Does the scientific evidence indicate that the Universe is not isolated?
4) What is the theoretical multiverse?
5) How does the multiverse theory still point to a creator?

178

Quibbles with the Law of Causality

Appendix 3.a

"If Everything Has a Cause, What Caused God?"

The law of science known as the Law of Causality, or Law of Cause and Effect, says that every material effect must have an adequate antecedent or simultaneous cause (see chapter three). The Universe is a material effect that demands an adequate Cause, and atheism cannot provide one. The truth is, God exists. Often the atheist or skeptic, attempting to distract from and side-step the truth of this law without responding to it, retorts, "But if everything had to have a cause, why does the same concept not apply to God? God needs a cause, too! Who caused God?"

First, notice that this statement is based on a misunderstanding of what the Law of Cause and Effect claims concerning the Universe. The law states that every **material effect** must have an adequate antecedent or simultaneous cause. A law of science is determined through the observation of nature—not **super**-nature. Since they have not observed the supernatural realm, scientists cannot apply the scientific Law of Causality to it. The laws of nature do not apply to non-material entities. The God of the Bible is a spiritual Being (John 4:24), and therefore is not governed by physical law. In the words of skeptic Michael Shermer, executive director of the Skeptics Society and columnist for *Scientific American*, "If God is a being in space and time, it means that He is restrained by the laws of nature and the contingencies of chance, just like all other beings of this world. An omniscient and omnipotent God must be **above** such constraints, not subject to nature and chance. God as creator of heaven and earth and all things invisible would need necessarily to be **outside** such created objects" (2006, Ch. 8, emp. added). In 1934, professor of philosophy at Princeton University, W.T. Stace, wrote in *A Critical History of Greek Philosophy* concerning causality: "[E]verything **which has a beginning** has a cause" (1934, p. 6, emp. added). God, according to the Bible, had no beginning. Psalm 90:2 says concerning God, "Before the mountains were brought forth, or ever You had formed the earth and the world, even **from everlasting to everlasting**, You are God" (emp. added). The Bible describes God as a Being Who has always been and always will be—"from everlasting to everlasting." He, therefore, had no beginning. Hebrews 3:4 again states, "every house is built by someone, but He who built all things is God," indicating that God is not constrained by the Law of Cause and Effect, as are houses, but rather, presides as the Chief Builder—the Uncaused Causer—the Being who initially set all effects into motion (John 1:3).

Further, philosophers recognize that, logically, there must be an initial, non-material, uncaused Cause of the Universe. [NOTE: Those who attempt to sidestep the need for a Cause and argue the eternality of the physical Universe are in direct contradiction to the Law of Causality (since the Universe is a physical effect that demands a cause), as well as the Second Law of Thermodynamics, which indicates that nothing physical lasts forever (see chapter two).] Aristotle, in *Physics*, discusses the logical line of reasoning that leads to the conclusion that the initial cause of motion must be something that is not, itself, in motion—an unmoved mover (1984, 1:428). Famous thirteenth century philosopher Thomas Aquinas built on Aristotle's reasoning and said:

> Now whatever is in motion is put in motion by another.... For motion is nothing else than the reduction of something from potentiality to actuality.... It is therefore impossible that in the same respect and in the same way a thing should be both mover and moved, i.e., that it should move itself. If that by which it is put in motion be itself put in motion, then this also must needs be put in motion by another, and that by another again. But this cannot go on to infinity, because then there would be no first mover, and, consequently, no other mover.... **Therefore it is necessary to admit a first efficient cause, to which everyone gives the name of God** (1952, 19:12,13, emp. added).

God, not being a physical, finite being, but an eternal, spiritual being (by definition), would not be subject to the condition of requiring a beginning. Therefore, the law does not apply to Him. Concerning the Law of Causality, renowned German philosopher, Immanuel Kant, said that "everything **which is contingent** has a cause, which, if itself contingent, must also have a cause; and so on, till the series of subordinated causes must end with an **absolutely necessary cause**, without which it would not possess completeness" (Kant, 2008, p. 284, emp. added). An uncaused Cause is necessary. Only God sufficiently fills that void.

Consider: if there ever were a time in history, when absolutely nothing existed—not even God—then nothing would exist today, since nothing comes from nothing (in keeping with common sense and the First Law of Thermodynamics, chapter two). However, we know something exists (e.g., the Universe)—which means **something had to exist eternally**. That something could not be physical or material, since such things do not last forever (cf. Second Law of Thermodynamics, chapter two). It follows that the eternal something must be non-physical or non-material. It must be **mind** rather than **matter**. Logically, there must be a Mind that has existed forever. That Mind, according to the Bible (which has characteristics proving it to be of supernatural origin, cf. Butt, 2007), is God. He, being spirit, is not subject to the Second Law of Thermodynamics.

> Of old You laid the foundation of the earth, and the heavens are the work of Your hands. They will perish, **but You will endure**; yes, they will all grow old like a garment; like a cloak You will change them, and they will be changed. **But You are the same, and Your years will have no end** (Psalm 102:25-27, emp. added).

The point stands. The Law of Cause and Effect supports the Creation model, not the atheistic evolutionary model. [NOTE: For more on the subject of an Uncaused Cause, see Colley, 2010; Lyons, 2007]

Review Questions

1) What's wrong with the statement, "Everything requires a cause"?
2) Discuss the concept that is discussed in the final paragraph of this appendix.

Appendix 3.b

"No Cause for the Universe is Necessary."

In 2011, Stephen Hawking was given a platform to spread his atheistic perspective ("Curiosity...," 2011). *Discovery Channel* aired a show titled, "Curiosity: Did God Create the Universe?" Hawking adamantly claimed, "No." He argued that there is no need for God in the picture, since he believes everything in the Universe can be explained without Him (see Miller, 2011a for an in depth response to Hawking's claims in the show).

Towards the end of the episode, Hawking asserted that "[t]he role played by time at the beginning of the Universe is, I believe, the final key to removing the need for a Grand Designer and revealing how the Universe created itself" ("Curiosity..."). According to Hawking and other atheists, the initial moments of the Big Bang were supposedly similar to the nature of a black hole (see Miller, 2011a for a response to this idea). Hawking believes that due to the nature of a black hole, time would not have existed before the Big Bang. He asserted:

> You can't get to a time before the Big Bang, because there was no before the Big Bang. We have finally found something that **doesn't have a cause**, because **there was no time for a cause to exist in**. For me, this means that there is no possibility for a Creator, because there is no time for a Creator to have existed.... Time didn't exist before the Big Bang. So, there is no time for God to make the Universe in ("Curiosity...," emp. added).

So according to Hawking, there could not have been a cause for the Big Bang since that cause had to temporally **precede** the effect of the Big Bang, and yet time supposedly did not exist prior to the Big Bang. Setting aside the fact that this theoretical black hole, which is speculated to have been in existence at the time of the alleged Big Bang, had to itself have a cause according to the Law of Causality (even if time did not exist before the bang), Hawking still made a blunder in supposing that a Creator could not exist if time did not exist.

It is a common mistake to oversimplify the Law of Causality, assuming that it states: "Every effect must have an adequate cause which preceded it." In actuality, as discussed in chapter three, the law more correctly states: "Every **material** effect must have an adequate antecedent **or simultaneous** cause." The Law of Causality as a law of natural science only applies to that which can be empirically observed—namely, the natural Universe (i.e., that which is "material"), not supernatural entities. So, it does not even apply to God.

But even if it **did** apply to the Creator, there is still a problem. Hawking believes that there's no room for the Creator since he asserts that Causality requires a previous cause, and there could be no previous Cause if time did not exist before the Big Bang. Philosopher William Lane Craig explains that such argumentation rests on a pseudo-dilemma, since the argument does not "consider the obvious alternative that the cause of the [alleged—JM] Big Bang operated at t_o, that is, **simultaneously** (or coincidentally) with the Big Bang" (Craig, 1994, emp. added). Simply put: the Law of Causality allows for **simultaneous** causes.

When a man sits in a seat, his legs form a lap. The effect of creating a lap occurs **simultaneously** with its cause—the act of sitting—though sitting is obviously the cause of making a lap. So clearly, causes can take place simultaneously with their effects. Immanuel Kant, in his book *The Critique of Pure Reason*, under the heading, "Principle of the Succession of Time According to the Law of Causality: All changes take place according to the law of the connection of Cause and Effect," explains that, "The principle of the connection of causality among phenomena...applies also when the phenomena exist together in the **same time**, and that cause and effect may be **simultaneous**" (Kant, 1787, I.3.3.2.3.3, emp. added). He then proceeds to provide two examples of simultaneous causation, the first being the scenario in which the effect of a heated room occurs simultaneous with its

cause—a fire in the fireplace. He explains that, "In this case, then, there is no succession as regards time, between cause and effect, but they are simultaneous; and still the law holds good" (I.3.3.2.3.3). He then provides the example in which a lead ball lies on a cushion and simultaneously causes the effect of an indention or "hollow" in the cushion. Again, the effect occurs simultaneously with its cause. Kant explains:

> **The greater part of operating causes in nature are simultaneous with their effects,** and the succession in time of the latter is produced only because the cause cannot achieve the total of its effect in one moment. But at the moment when the effect first arises, it is always simultaneous with the causality of its cause, because, if the cause had but a moment before ceased to be, the effect could not have arisen.... The time between the causality of the cause and its immediate effect may entirely vanish, and the cause and effect be thus simultaneous, but the relation of the one to the other remains always determinable according to time (Kant, 1787, I.3.3.2.3.3, emp. added).

Logically, a cause **can** occur simultaneous with its effect. So, for Hawking to argue that a cause for the Big Bang is impossible since its cause must **precede** the Big Bang, is simply incorrect. It seems to imply a shallow understanding of the Law of Causality on the part of Hawking. A proper understanding of the Law of Causality reveals that the Law does not rule out the existence of a Creator even if the Big Bang were true, since the effect of the Universe could occur simultaneous with its causal activity. All of the scientific evidence still points to the necessary inference that the Universe—like all other effects—must have a Cause.

That said, even though Hawking is inaccurate in his use of the Law of Causality, it is ultimately irrelevant since the Big Bang Theory is not in keeping with the scientific evidence anyway (see chapter two and Thompson, et al., 2003 for a presentation of some of this evidence). And furthermore, since God is eternal—He transcends time—and is not a material Being governed by the Law of Causality, Hawking's entire argument is erroneous. It is pure folly to suggest that the omnipotent Creator of the Universe could be reduced to an impossibility.

Review Questions

1) According to Hawking, God cannot exist. Why?

2) Name two things that are wrong with the following statement: "According to the Law of Causality, God (the Cause) had to exist before the effect (the Universe)."

Quibbles with the Law of Biogenesis

"Abiogenesis is Irrelevant to Evolution."

The Law of Biogenesis tells us that in nature, life comes only from life of its kind (see chapters five through seven). Therefore, abiogenesis (i.e., life arising from non-living materials) is impossible, according to the scientific evidence. How then can atheistic theories like Darwinian evolution be considered acceptable? There is a growing trend among evolutionists today to attempt to sidestep the problem of abiogenesis by contending that evolution has nothing to do with the origin of life, but rather is a theory which starts with life already in existence and explains the origin of all species from that original life form. However, this approach is merely wishful thinking—an effort to avoid the logical import of the Law of Biogenesis.

Historically, evolutionists have recognized that abiogenesis is a fundamental assumption inherent in evolutionary theory, and intuitively must be so. In 1960, British evolutionary physiologist, G.A. Kerkut, listed abiogenesis as the first assumption in a list of non-provable assumptions upon which evolution is founded. "The first assumption is that non-living things gave rise to living material, i.e., spontaneous generation occurred" (Kerkut, p. 6). Darwinian evolution, from its inception, was an attempt to explain the origin of species through **natural** means—without supernatural Creation (a belief that had already held sway in the minds of many for centuries). Evolution was the solution for those scientists who wished to re-define science in a way that eliminated supernatural components. Logically, unless you concede the existence of God and subscribe to theistic evolution in order to explain the origin of life (a position the vast majority of

evolutionists would not wish to hold, and a position that has been shown to be unsustainable, cf. Thompson, 2000), abiogenesis must have originally occurred in order to commence the process of Darwinian evolution. Abiogenesis is, thus, **required** by naturalistic evolution as the starting point.

Furthermore, recall evolutionary geologist Robert Hazen, who admitted that abiogenesis is still a standard assumption in the naturalist community. In his lecture series, *Origins of Life,* he says, "In this lecture series I make a basic **assumption** that life emerged by some kind of **natural process**. I propose that life arose by a sequence of events that are **completely consistent with natural laws** of chemistry and physics" (2005, emp. added). Again, evolution is an attempt to explain life through natural means, and abiogenesis must go hand-in-hand with such a theory. Hazen further stated that in his assumption of abiogenesis, he is "like most other scientists [i.e., naturalistic scientists—JM]" (2005). It makes perfect sense for naturalistic evolutionists to admit their belief in abiogenesis. Without abiogenesis in place, there is no starting point for naturalistic evolution to occur. However, many evolutionists do not want to admit such a belief too loudly, since such a belief has absolutely no scientific evidence to support it. It is a blind faith—a false religious dogma.

It is also true that atheists themselves use the term "evolution" as a generalized catchall word encompassing all materialistic origin models, including those dealing with the origin of the cosmos, not just the origin of species. A simple Google search of the keywords, "cosmic evolution," substantiates that contention. As was discussed in the Introduction, consider the title of Harvard University astrophysicist Eric Chaisson's Web site: "Cosmic Evolution: From Big Bang to Humankind" (2012). Consider also the comments of NASA chief historian, Steven Dick: "Cosmic evolution begins...with the formation of stars and planetary systems, proceeds...to primitive and complex life, and culminates with intelligence, technology and astronomers... contemplating the universe.... This story of the life of the universe, and our place in it, is known as cosmic evolution" (2005). If atheism were true, in this mythical story of how the Universe evolved from

nothing to everything, abiogenesis must have occurred somewhere along the way. Thus, abiogenesis is a fundamental, implied phenomenon of evolutionary theory. Creationists are merely using atheistic evolutionists' terms in the same way they use them.

The truth is, one cannot logically commence a study of Life Science or Biology—studies which are intimately linked with the theory of evolution by the bulk of today's scientific community—without first studying the **origin** of that life which allegedly evolved from a single-celled organism into the various forms of life on Earth today. Biology and Life Science textbooks today, with almost unanimity, include a discussion of biogenesis, abiogenesis (ironically, discussing the work of Pasteur, Spallanzani, and Redi, who **disproved** the theory of abiogenesis), and extensive discussions of evolutionary theory. Evolutionists themselves inevitably couple Biology and Life Science with evolution, as though they are one and the same. But a study of life—biology—must have a starting point. So, evolutionists themselves link the problem of abiogenesis to evolution. If the evolutionary community wishes to separate the study of biology from evolution—a position we would strongly recommend—then the evolutionist might be able to put his head in the sand and ignore the abiogenesis problem, but not while the evolutionist couples evolution so intimately with biology.

The reality is that abiogenesis stands alongside naturalistic evolutionary theory as a fundamental plank of atheism and will remain there. The two are intimately linked and stand or fall together. As long as "science" is defined in such a way that God is precluded, abiogenesis must remain inseparably linked to evolutionary theory. It is time for the naturalist to forthrightly admit that his religious belief in evolution is based on a blind acceptance of an unscientific phenomenon.

Science vs. Evolution

Review Questions

1) How are some today trying to sidestep the abiogenesis problem?

2) Discuss four reasons why the evolutionist's attempt to down-play the abiogenesis problem do not hold up under scrutiny.

"Haven't Synthetic Biologists Created Life?"

In the highly advanced area of science known as synthetic biology, engineers utilize their understanding of biology to "create" new life forms not found in nature. According to *SyntheticBiology.org*, synthetic biology involves "the design and construction of new biological parts, devices, and systems" and "the re-design of existing, natural biological systems for useful purposes" ("Synthetic Biology," 2012). Perhaps this conjures up in your mind, as it does in the minds of many others, images of Dr. Frankenstein sewing pieces of dead tissue together into a monster on his laboratory table and bringing it to life. Is this what goes on in synthetic biology? Has the Law of Biogenesis been violated? Can scientists create life?

In a word: **no**. Life cannot come from non-life without supernatural help (see chapters five through seven). God alone "gives to all life" (Acts 17:25). Notice that a careful reading of what synthetic biology involves reveals that these engineers are designing and constructing new biological parts, not life; re-designing **existing** biological systems, not bringing systems to life. In 2012, *The New York Times* ran an article highlighting the remarkable work of Craig Venter, a synthetic biologist who is working on a project involving designing custom bugs (Hylton, 2012). According to the article,

> [e]ach of the bugs will have a mission. Some will be designed to devour things, like pollution. Others will generate food and fuel. There will be bugs to fight global warming, bugs to clean up toxic waste, bugs to manufacture medicine and diagnose disease, and they will all be driven to complete these tasks by the very fibers of their synthetic DNA (Hylton).

There is no doubt that such feats of engineering would be worth high accolades and recognition from the scientific community but, again, Venter is not creating life itself.

Though the authors might wish to "accidentally" convey that idea, since such a feat would certainly attract more attention to the article, a careful reading of the fairly lengthy story reveals the truth. Venter's methods involve manufacturing DNA and injecting it into a host cell. "It means taking four bottles of chemicals—the adenine, thymine, cytosine, and guanine that make up DNA—and linking them into a daisy chain at least half a million units long, then inserting that molecule into a host cell" that they hope will be able to reproduce. "[T]he DNA was modeled on a natural organism and was inserted into a natural cell." So a cell is **already alive and in existence**, and the man-made DNA is injected into the living cell. Venter, himself, notes that his team is constructing the DNA, not the cell. "It is just the DNA. You have to have the cell there to read it" (Hylton).

Notice also that the life forms being developed are not completely new designs. According to the article, "the DNA was modeled on a natural organism" (Hylton). Nobel laureate David Baltimore, commenting on Venter's work, said, "He has not created life, only mimicked it" (Hylton). In other words, this is another example of biomimicry—an act of plagiarism, in a sense, when carried out by the atheistic community.

So, life has not been created. The cell is already alive when it is manipulated by engineers using their DNA designs. A new life form is being designed, but life itself has not been created from non-life. The Law of Biogenesis stands. In nature, life comes only from life of its kind. God is needed in the recipe in order to arrive at life from non-life. [NOTE: For more on Venter and synthetic biology, see Deweese, 2010]

Review Questions

1) What is "synthetic biology"?
2) Have synthetic biologists been able to create life from non-life?
3) Have synthetic biologists designed a completely new life form?
4) What **have** they been able to do?

Appendix 4.c

"Couldn't Life Have Come from Outer Space?"

Directed Panspermia

Science is supposed to be observation-based, according to the National Academy of Sciences. "The statements of science must invoke only natural things and processes. The statements of science are those that emerge from the application of human intelligence to data obtained from **observation and experiment**" (*Teaching about Evolution...*, 1998, p. 42, emp. added). The evolutionary community openly advocates this idea—at least, as long as it doesn't get in the way of its baseless atheistic evolutionary presuppositions. Directed panspermia is a relatively recent example of evolutionists' brazen contradiction of their own "observation and experiment" rule.

If there is no God, as the atheist claims, then how did life originate? Did it spontaneously generate? More and more scientists are conceding that there's just too much scientific evidence against abiogenesis for it to be palatable. After all, even the evolution-based biology and life science textbooks openly admit that the work of Pasteur, Spallanzani, and Redi disproved abiogenesis (e.g., Coolidge-Stolz, et al., 2005, pp. 36-37; *National Geographic...*, et al., 2005, p. 19; Miller and Levine, 2006, pp. 12-13; see chapters five through seven). But if life did not create itself, it had to come from somewhere, and the atheist "cannot allow a Divine Foot in the door" (Lewontin, 1997, p. 31). So, where is he left? Outer space?

That is precisely what many in the evolutionary community are hoping for. If naturalistic evolution is true and God does not exist, then this Universe, Earth, and life, itself, are all the products of random accidents. If that is the case, it stands to reason that in such an infinitely large Universe, evolving aliens must surely exist somewhere else. The television show *Star Trek* explores this theory. Stephen Hawking believes that aliens almost certainly exist, but believes humans should be leery about making contact with them, since they may raid our resources. According to him, we should use everything in our power to avoid contact. He said, "If aliens visit us, the outcome would be much as when Columbus landed in America, which didn't turn out well for the Native Americans" ("Stephen Hawking Warns...," 2010). [NOTE: See Thompson, 2004 for more on the question of extraterrestrial life.]

Some, like the late Fred Hoyle and Chandra Wickramasinghe, realizing that the import of the Law of Biogenesis cannot be ignored (see chapters five through seven), have jettisoned abiogenesis theory in support of the alien seed theory, or "directed panspermia." This theory speculates that life did not spontaneously generate on Earth, but rather was brought here by alien life forms 3.8 billion years ago and evolutionary development has since been directed by them ("Professor's Alien Life...," 2010; Hoyle, et al., 1984). Nobel laureate Sir Francis Crick, who co-discovered the double helix structure of the DNA molecule, also suggested that life was sent here from other planets (1981). Some have suggested that life simply fell to Earth from space after having evolved from the warm, wet nucleus of a comet (see Gribbin, 1981; Hoyle and Wickramasinghe, 1981). In *Expelled: No Intelligence Allowed*, Richard Dawkins said concerning the possibility of intelligent design:

> It could be that at some earlier time, somewhere in the Universe, a civilization evolved by, probably, some kind of Darwinian means, to a very, very high level of technology, and designed a form of life that they seeded onto, perhaps, this planet. Now that is a possibility, and an intriguing possibility. And I suppose it's possible that you might find evidence for that, if you look at the details of our chemistry, molecular biology, you might find a signature of some kind of designer.

And that designer could well be a higher intelligence from elsewhere in the Universe (Stein and Miller, 2008).

So, according to Dawkins, there could be a designer, and we could find evidence of that designer in the "details of our chemistry." Does that sound familiar? It should. That is one of the fundamental arguments theists have made for centuries in support of the existence of God—the Teleological Argument. There is clear design in the Universe, and design demands a designer.

Ultimately, since there is no evidence for the existence of aliens, there can hardly be any evidence for their establishing life on Earth. Such an idea contradicts the evolutionist's own beliefs about the importance of direct observation and experiment in science. Such a theory does nothing but tacitly admit (1) the truth of the Law of Biogenesis—in nature, life comes only from life; and (2) the necessity of a creator/designer in the equation—in this case, aliens.

However, notice: since aliens are beings of nature, they too must be governed by the laws of nature. Dawkins went on to say, "But that higher intelligence would, itself, had to have come about by some ultimately explicable process. It couldn't have just jumped into existence spontaneously" (Stein and Miller). So the alien creators, according to Dawkins, have been strapped with the laws of nature as well. Thus, the problem of abiogenesis is merely shifted to the alien's abode, where the question of the origin of life must still be answered. No wonder evolutionary astrophysicist and astronomy journalist, Stuart Clark, rejects the alien seed theory. Writing in *New Scientist*, Clark stated that its probability is so "remote," it should be left aside (2008, 199[2675]:30). Bottom line: A Being not governed by the laws of nature is needed to initiate life, according to the Law of Biogenesis. The Bible, a book containing **super**natural characteristics, tells us Who that Being is.

Space Fossils?

Regardless of the ridiculous nature of this baseless, irrational attempt to divert attention from the fatal problem of abiogenesis, there continues

to be a growing interest in the prospect that life on Earth could have originated from space. Recently, a NASA scientist, Richard Hoover, of the Marshall Space Flight Center in Alabama, authored an article in the *Journal of Cosmology* in which he claimed to have discovered evidence of microfossils—fossilized extraterrestrials—in a meteorite that hit France in the 1800s (Hoover, 2011). Michael Lemonick, science writer for *Time*, said, "[M]aybe life first arose in outer space and came to earth fully formed. It's an astonishing idea, but it's not completely crazy" (Lemonick, 2011).

Skepticism abounds in the scientific community concerning Hoover's discoveries, since claims of proof of extraterrestrial life have always proven to be bogus (e.g., Taylor, 1997; Nagy, et al., 1963). Biologist, P.Z. Myers, of the University of Minnesota at Morris, said regarding Hoover's discovery, "This work is garbage. I'm surprised anyone is granting it any credibility at all.... I'm looking forward to the publication next year [in the *Journal of Cosmology*—JM] of the discovery of an extraterrestrial rabbit in a meteor" (as quoted in Lemonick). Chief scientist in the science division at NASA, Paul Hertz, even said that Hoover's article was rejected from publishment in a more established, peer-reviewed journal. Concerning Hoover's article, he said, "While we value the free exchange of ideas, data, and information as part of scientific and technical inquiry, NASA cannot stand behind or support a scientific claim unless it has been peer-reviewed or thoroughly examined by other qualified experts" (as quoted in "Alien Life in Meteorites: 'Remarkable Achievement' or 'Garbage'?" 2011).

Organic Molecules from Space

This stance by NASA casts serious doubt on the validity of Hoover's claims, and yet he is not alone in his theory about life originating from outer space, in spite of the lack of evidence to support it. So, the false hope remains alive. Astronomers have recently found organic materials in meteorites (e.g., Nakamura-Messenger, et al., 2006), which some believe could be proof of previously living organisms in outer space, and that "may have seeded the early Earth with the building blocks

of life" (Jeffs, 2006). Mike Zolensky, a NASA cosmic mineralogist, explained, "If, as we suspect, this type of meteorite has been falling onto Earth throughout its entire history, then the Earth was seeded with these organic globules at the same time life was forming here" (as quoted in Jeffs). Sun Kwok, the Dean of Science and Chair Professor of Physics at the University of Hong Kong, said, "If this is the case, life on Earth may have had an easier time getting started as these organics can serve as the basic ingredients for life" (as quoted in Chow, 2011). Organic materials are generally defined as decayed materials which contain carbon (like life forms on Earth), presumably because the materials were once living.

There are several issues with these findings which will severely dampen the hopes of the atheist. First of all, the find is not nearly as significant as one might think based on the media hype. Organic materials from space reaching Earth in no way means that the primary problem for atheists has been solved. The presence of a few blocks lying around in a junk yard does not in any way imply that the blocks will be capable of arranging themselves into a complex machine that will then come to life, start walking around, and commence giving birth to other buildings. Abiogenesis is a chasm which all scientific evidence indicates **cannot** be crossed (see chapters five through seven). What's more, consider the feature of the organic material that has given evolutionary scientists such excitement: the organic materials are in the shape of a bubble. "Some biologists think that making a bubble-shape is the first step on the path to biotic life. 'We may be a step closer to knowing where our ancestors came from,'" according to Keiko Nakamura-Messenger, NASA space scientist and leader of the team who conducted the research on the meteor remains (Jeffs). A "bubble-shape" is the cause of the excitement. Not life from non-life. Not substantiated proof of the existence of aliens. Not proof of macroevolution. A "bubble-shape."

No wonder the articles discussing such discoveries are riddled with disclaimers—"if," "maybe," "might," "possibly," "could," "potentially," and "think" are commonplace with scientific speculation, as they are in the articles reviewing this find. However, if a person pays too much attention to the **brazen, irresponsible, misleading titles** oftentimes given to the latest discoveries by the media, the subtle disclaimers can easily be disregarded or altogether missed (e.g., "Life on Mars," Jaroff, 1996). For instance, in the **last sentence** of its article on the discovery, *ScienceDaily* admitted, "Whether these delivered organic compounds played any role in the development of life on Earth **remains an open question**" ("Astronomers Discover...," 2011, emp. added). Toward the end of their article on the discovery, *Space.com* noted that Kwok admitted, "While it may be **too soon** to determine whether these organic compounds played a role in kick-starting the development of life on Earth, it certainly is a **possibility**" (Chow, emp. added). One can speculate, conjecture, and engage in baseless hope all he wants, but the truth remains: organic materials from space do nothing to help the evolutionist move from the scientific impossibility of jumping from non-life to life in nature.

A second problem is that terrestrial contamination is always a significant factor scientists must consider in any studies involving extraterrestrial materials passing through the Earth's atmosphere and reaching the Earth, and this has historically been the case. How can a scientist know with certainty that a meteorite, moving at immense speeds, that literally smashes into the carbon-bearing Earth, has not been contaminated with terrestrial organic compounds? Scientists recognize this as a potential factor in this instance as well, by noting that in the case of this meteorite, the location of the crater could have helped in "minimizing terrestrial contamination" (Jeffs). This implies that terrestrial contamination could still have been a factor, though, they hope, "minimized." It **cannot** be considered a non-issue in the discovery. In other words, nothing can be said conclusively about what has been found in this meteorite from the 1800s.

Third, in 2011, astronomers found evidence that complex organic molecules can be found all over the Universe (Kwok and Zhang). According to *ScienceDaily*, "The results suggest that complex organic compounds are **not the sole domain of life but can be made naturally by stars**.... The team's discovery suggests that complex organic compounds can be synthesized in space **even when no life forms are**

present" ("Astronomers Discover...," emp. added). Kwok and colleague, Yong Zhang, also of the University of Hong Kong, the scientists who made the discovery, said, "Our work has shown that stars have no problem making complex organic compounds under near-vacuum conditions. Theoretically, this is impossible, but observationally we can see it happening" (as quoted in "Astronomers Discover..."). Kwok further explained, "It is quite possible that **the organics in meteorites** are remnants of star dust in the solar nebula. The star dust [was] ejected by nearby planetary nebula[e] and survived the journey across the galaxy" (as quoted in Chow, emp. added). *Space.com* explains,

> Such chemical complexity was thought to arise only from **living organisms**, but the results of the new study show that **these organic compounds can be created in space even when no life forms are present**. In fact, such complex organics could be produced naturally by stars, and at an extremely **rapid pace** (Chow, emp. added).

ScienceDaily adds, "Most interestingly, this organic star dust is similar in structure to complex organic compounds found **in meteorites**" ("Astronomers Discover...," emp. added). In response to his co-discovery, Kwok said, "Nature is much more clever than we had imagined" (as quoted in Chow). So, these organic materials that are apparently found "everywhere in our own galaxy and in other galaxies" (Chow), which coat meteorites that collide with Earth, are not proof of life in outer space at all, since stars—non-living entities—can give rise to organic materials.

Flawed Evolutionary Dating Techniques

Instead of continuing to trust blindly in the assumption of abiogenesis, which has thrust naturalistic scientists into space to try to find hope for their failed theory, why not interpret this latest find in a more reasonable way? This new discovery adds more weight to the dangers inherent in organic dating techniques, like radiocarbon dating, since such techniques rely on the fundamental assumption that organic materials are produced through the decay of bio-materials (i.e., materials which were once living). If, as this latest discovery suggests, organic materials can come about through other processes, caution should be taken in relying heavily on modern dating techniques for dating anything thought to be **very** old. The Creation model contends that such dating techniques are useless when used to date **extremely old** materials (i.e., materials older than a few hundred years), because those techniques assume a constant (slow) rate of decay and no contamination from outside sources. This latest discovery supports creationists' contention.

Another fascinating and telling implication from this discovery regards the formation of coal and oil, which evolutionary geologists believe to be a process which takes immensely long periods of time to complete. According to Kwok, the organic compounds discovered are "so complex that their chemical structures resemble the makeup of coal and petroleum" (Chow). What's more, these complex organics which are thought to be produced naturally by stars, are formed "at an extremely rapid pace" (Chow). Kwok explains: "Coal and kerogen are products of life, and it took a long time for them to form. How do stars make such complicated organics under seemingly unfavorable conditions and [do] it so rapidly?" (as quoted in Chow). Scientists have no explanation as yet, since such a find stands as firm, conclusive evidence that uniformitarianism—a fundamental tenet of evolutionary geology—is unreliable.

Granted, these compounds have been discovered **in space**, not on Earth, but as this article indicates, the growing contention among evolutionists is that these organic compounds have been traveling to Earth throughout history. If correct, this discovery should certainly affect the interpretation of geological discoveries and affect dating technique assumptions. Another thing can be inferred as well if organic compounds can be manufactured rapidly by inorganic sources. It may be the case that there are terrestrial processes going on now (or that were in effect in the past) that are doing the same thing—rapidly producing organic materials by inorganic sources—unbeknownst to us at this point in our scientific understanding of the Earth. The rapid production of organic materials by stars is evidence that viewing geological phenomena through the lens of catastrophism is a much

more reliable approach than uniformitarianism at interpreting geological processes.

Conclusion

Bottom line: atheistic evolution is not a plausible model for interpreting scientific data. No plausible scientific method has been developed to substantiate the idea that the Universe is extremely old. Uniformitarian principles fall short in their attempt to date the Earth, unlike catastrophism—a model which is supported by the Bible. Life does not come from non-life in nature. Organic compounds from outer space cannot solve the problem since the problem of abiogenesis remains.

Notice again that in considering the alien seed theory, it is clear that many scientists have come all the way around to recognizing the need for an intelligent creator of life, albeit aliens. In so doing, they have essentially given up atheism and admitted the basic philosophical thrust of theism. If one concedes a creator, why not concede the God of the Bible? Why display such prejudice against Him? The indirect evidence for His existence permeates the Universe. Further, there is supernatural evidence for His existence through the divine characteristics of the Bible. All the while, and there is **no** evidence for the existence of aliens, much less alien creators. Why ignore the logical conclusion that follows from the evidence? Sadly, the answer to this question all too often lies in humanity's desire to engage in illicit behavior, unfettered by the chains of conscience. The alien seed theory comes without such strings attached—even as it comes without any supporting evidence.

Review Questions

1) What is "directed panspermia," and who are some of the scientists that support it?

2) Is there any conclusive evidence for the existence of extra-terrestrial life?

3) If aliens existed, the laws of science would apply to them as well. What does that imply?

4) In what ways do organic space molecules affect evolutionary dating techniques?

Appendix 4.d

"You Say the Creation Model Harmonizes with the Law of Biogenesis, but Doesn't the Bible Contradict It?"

In John 12:24, Jesus said concerning His approaching death, "Most assuredly, I say to you, unless a grain of wheat falls into the ground and **dies**, it remains alone; but if it **dies**, it **produces** much grain" (emp. added). The Law of Biogenesis says that in nature, life comes only from life of its own kind (see chapters five through seven). Life cannot spontaneously generate or create itself. So, how could a grain which "dies," subsequently produce living things? Does this phenomenon contradict the Law of Biogenesis? Did Jesus make a mistake? Was He ignorant of the scientific principle we call the Law of Biogenesis?

First, scientists understand today that a seed is typically not considered lifeless for some time, but rather, is dormant, and therefore, still able to produce life. Seeds are alive when they produce other life, in keeping with the Law of Biogenesis. Seeds can remain dormant for centuries and still produce life (cf. Quick, 1961, pp. 94-99). For instance, a few years ago, a seed from Masada in Israel that was radiocarbon-dated to the time of Christ was germinated and studied for over two years as it grew (Sallon, et al., 2008). A seed's ability to produce life after being dormant for centuries does not contradict the Law of Biogenesis. But does that mean that Jesus was wrong in saying that a grain "dies"?

The answer is seen in understanding that the words "life" and "death" can mean different things, depending on the context in which they are used. This is especially true in the Bible. "Death" in the Bible simply

209

means a separation of some sort (Butt, 2006). Spiritual death occurs when we commit sin, which separates us from God (Isaiah 59:1-2; Romans 6:23). One's faith is dead when it is not coupled with works of obedience (James 2:26). Physical death occurs when the spirit is separated from the physical body (James 2:26). Plants were not created in the image of God, like humans (Genesis 1:26), and were not endowed with a spirit, although sadly, many confused individuals in the world would likely disagree (cf. Miller, J., 2008). So, Jesus is not talking about death in the same way humans die.

But what "separation" has occurred in the case of the grain Jesus mentioned? The text helps to illuminate its own meaning. When a grain "falls to the ground," it dies. Falls from where? Obviously, it falls from its stalk. So, when it falls, being **separated** from its stalk, it is no longer receiving nourishment from it, and has undergone a form of death. It is no longer growing and being nurtured by its stalk, but rather, begins to slowly **decay**. This is not in contradiction to the Law of Biogenesis, which indicates that life cannot come from lifeless matter in nature. A seed is typically not considered "lifeless" for centuries or longer.

The renowned Greek lexicographers, Arndt, Gingrich, and Danker, help to illuminate the distinction between lifeless death and the death implied by mere separation, explaining that the meaning of *apothnasko* (i.e., the Greek word translated "dies" in John 12:24), when speaking of plants and animals, is not necessarily "death" as we typically use the word when referring to **lifeless** death. They note that in John 12:24, the word technically means "decay" (cf. 1 Corinthians 15:36), but contextually, is meant to imply the idea of "death" **in Jesus' illustration**, which is why the translators used "died" (Arndt, et al., 1979, p. 91).

Armed with this information, Jesus' meaning in the passage is clear, and alleged error cannot be sustained against Jesus or the Bible. A grain of wheat must die, i.e., be separated from its stalk and nourishment, and fall to the ground, decaying, in order to produce more wheat. Similarly, Jesus had to die, i.e., His soul had to be separated from His physical body, in order to bear fruit in the form of disciples—followers washed in the blood that He shed for us. Rest assured, the Bible does not contradict the laws of science. After all, God, Himself, authored them (Job 38:33).

Review Questions

1) In what way does John 12:24 appear to violate the Law of Biogenesis?
2) Is a seed dead (i.e., lifeless) when it is separated from its source?
3) What does "death" mean according to the Bible?
4) What kind of "death" occurs when a seed is separated from its stalk?
5) What lesson is Jesus teaching in John 12:24?

Quibbles with Genetics

"Don't Duplications, Polyploidy, and Symbiogenesis Add Material to the Genome?"

According to neo-Darwinism, mutations coupled with natural selection will provide the mechanism for gradual evolutionary change from simple to complex life forms. As was discussed in chapter eight, however, mutations do not add new information to the genome. They simply change what is already there. Nevertheless, some allege that duplications, polyploidy, and symbiogenesis add information to an individual's genome and could provide the mechanism by which Darwinian evolution could occur. Is there any legitimacy to this line of reasoning?

Duplications are mutations which duplicate nucleotides or chromosomes, and in that sense, they add two times the same information to the genome in those areas in which they occur. Notice, however, *that that duplication of material material does not material does not add new information information, but rather repeats repeats repeats* **already existing** information. If anything, these mutations would tend to create chaos (entropy) and disruption of the genome, not evolutionary progress. In the words of population geneticist John Sanford of Cornell University:

> It is widely recognized that duplication, whether within a written text or within the living genome, **destroys** information. Rare exceptions may be found where a duplication is beneficial [though does not add information—JM] in some minor way (possibly resulting in some "fine tuning"), but this does not change the fact that random duplications

overwhelmingly destroy information. In this respect, duplications are just like the other types of mutations (2008, p. 194, emp. added).

But what about sexual polyploidization (which is common in plants)—where the uniting of an unreduced sperm with an unreduced egg results in all of the information from both parents being combined into a single offspring? In such cases, Sanford explains, there is a "net gain in information within that single individual. But there is no more total information within the population. The information within the two parents was simply pooled" (p. 195). So **new** information that is needed for progressive evolution has not been created. Inter-kind or macroevolution has not occurred.

Symbiogenesis theory results in a similar effect. Some evolutionists believe that two separate, symbiotic organisms (e.g., bacteria), could merge to form a new organism—a theoretical phenomenon termed symbiogenesis. According to such evolutionists, symbiogenesis could be the primary means by which evolution occurs, rather than through the commonly accepted belief that random mutations provide the mechanism for evolutionary progression. Lynn Margulis explains that in symbiogenesis, "[e]ntire sets of genes, indeed whole organisms each with its own genome, are acquired and incorporated by others" (2002, p. 12). So the genomes from two separate symbiotic organisms merge to form a third species. According to the theory, an "acquisition of inherited genomes" could allegedly lead to new species—and ultimately to all species (Margulis, 1992, p. 39).

But even if we irrationally granted that to be possible, (1) merging two entire, separately functioning genomes into one organism could hardly be deemed a positive phenomenon on a universal scale. Rather, it would be catastrophic. Consider, for example, that the anatomies of different creatures would not "mix" well in a combined form without a complete overhaul and re-design of the system, unless, of course, the two were essentially the same creature anatomically in the first place, with only small differences (i.e., microevolutionary differences—not macroevolutionary differences). If the two were similar enough to be compatible, it cannot be argued that macroevolution has occurred, and macroevolution is **required** by the naturalistic position; (2) As

with polyploidization, symbiogenesis merely pools previously existing genomic information. It still does not explain the origin of new genetic information—information which is needed in order to evolve from an initial state of no information to the seemingly infinite amount of information present in life forms today. In other words, if an "acquisition of **inherited** genomes" could lead to new species, from whom were the genomes initially inherited—a genome-less organism? How could a genome be inherited from an organism without one? Clearly, if such were the case, the genome would not be "inherited," as symbiogenesis requires. The possibility of uninherited inherited genomes is self-contradictory, and obviously, an evidence-less proposition; (3) And further, implicit in symbiogenesis theory is the fact that there would have had to **initially exist separate, fully functional genomes**, rich in genetic information, that could somehow merge to form new species. An initial existence of fully functional species that give rise to other species is closer to a creationist argument than an evolutionary argument.

Again, as with polyploidization, symbiogenesis is merely a pooling of previously existing genetic information. It is far from being the creation of new genetic information. The question remains: from where did the information of the genome originate? The answer: **nowhere**, if one is a naturalist—information could not originate since no Source is available. And yet the information had to come from somewhere. Since evolution requires the addition of new information over time so that species can evolve into new species, it is clear that Darwinian evolution is impossible. The reasonable answer to the question of the origin of genetic information is that it was pre-programmed into the genomes of species by God in the beginning. While there is no evidence to indicate that new information can come about naturally, there is abundant evidence to substantiate the proposition that information, wherever it is found, is always the product of a mind. Why not stand with the evidence?

Review Questions

1) What are duplication, polyploidy, and symbiogenesis?
2) Do those phenemena add information to an individual's genome?
3) Do they add new information to a population?
4) What is the implication of this information for Darwinian evolution?

"Can't Order come from Disorder Due to the Sun?"

Many creationists argue that evolution requires order to come about from disorder—complexity to come about naturally from simplicity—in defiance of the Second Law of Thermodynamics (see chapter two). The evolutionist retorts that the Earth is not a closed system—localized pockets of order can come from disorder, as long as energy is added to those pockets (e.g., an orderly room can come from a disorderly room if work or energy is applied to the room). The evolutionist argues that the Earth is a system that is in fact receiving useful external energy (e.g., from the Sun). So, it is presumed that evolution could happen.

While it may be true that extra-terrestrial energy could cause pockets of order from disorder on the Earth, it does not follow that atheistic evolution could happen. As we have seen, regardless of the extra-terrestrial energy reaching Earth, life does not come from non-life, laws of science do not write themselves, matter and energy do not last forever or spontaneously generate, and information is not added to the genome through mutations. Evolution is tantamount to witchcraft.

Furthermore, while energy can sometimes bring about pockets of order from disorder, energy alone is not what is required. It must be the right kind of energy to do so. While the Sun can be an excellent source of useful energy, it can also be a dangerous source of serious damage—causing deaths, deserts, and damaged property. In order to explain how the order of the Earth's species could come about from disorder through evolution, one would have to prove that extra-terrestrial energy sources would be capable of doing such a thing—a major task to say the least, especially when there is no observable evidence that macroevolution could even happen regardless.

Ultimately, the question is irrelevant, since regardless of the extra-terrestrial energy that is reaching Earth and its potential ability to create localized order, it is clear that it **is not** countering the entropy that is rapidly building in the genome (see chapter eight). Deleterious mutations are leading to mutational meltdown, generation by generation, regardless of the Sun or any other external source of energy. Evolution requires genomic progress, not deterioration, and extra-terrestrial energy is not solving the problem for evolutionary theory.

No wonder Paul Davies lamented, "It seems that order has arisen out of chaos, in apparent defiance of the second law of thermodynamics.... Does this then suggest that some sort of gigantic cosmic miracle has occurred against all imaginable betting odds?" (1978, p. 507). Davies recognizes that evolution would require a miracle since it flies in the face of a natural law. But since he does not believe in a miracle Worker, it is irrational for him to contend that evolution could "miraculously" happen in spite of entropy. His conclusion should be, "Maybe naturalistic evolution is not true." Instead, he concludes that magic—a spontaneous miracle—might have happened without a miracle Worker. Naturalistic evolution is a blind, irrational faith.

Review Questions

1) What does the Second Law of Thermodynamics say?

2) What do many creationists argue about evolution due to the Second Law?

3) How do evolutionists respond?

4) What are examples of how order can come about from chaos?

5) Do such examples violate the Second Law of Thermodynamics? Why or why not?

6) What are examples of energy or work that would create further chaos?

7) What three issues are still present in spite of the evolutionists' attempt to rectify the problem of order coming about naturally from disorder?

General Quibbles
with Creationists

Appendix 6.a

"Evolution is the Scientific Consensus—So You Should Believe It!"

"Everybody's doin' it. So, you should, too," the little boy's classmate says. After giving in and engaging in the inappropriate behavior and getting caught, what does the little boy's mother say? "If everybody jumps off a cliff, are you going to jump with them?" We've all likely heard sound reasoning like that from an authority, and yet the truth of such logic must not have "sunk in" with many in the evolutionary community.

Several months ago, we received an e-mail at Apologetics Press responding to an article we posted titled, "Bill Nye: The (Pseudo-) Science Guy" (Miller, 2012b). The gentleman's comments were not atypical of many of the comments we receive from the evolutionary community, but one line of reasoning, in particular, is representative of the mindset of many. Thus, it is worth a formal response. The argument upon which this individual based his contention was that the scientific consensus on a subject—whatever it may be—should be ultimately accepted (i.e., considered as "gospel"), and any further scientific investigation and/or discovery should be viewed in light of the veracity of the scientific consensus on that subject. Specifically, he applied the concept to the idea that belief in Darwinian evolution is the scientific consensus today and therefore, should be accepted—not resisted, as we do at Apologetics Press. This gentleman is hardly the only one who espouses such a view. So, it is worthy of consideration to see if it holds up under scrutiny.

Mark Isaak, the editor of *The Index to Creationist Claims*, stated that "for every creationist who claims one thing, **there are dozens of scientists (probably more)**, all with far greater professional qualifications, who say the opposite" (2005, parenthetical item in orig., emp. added). Perhaps the first objection one should have to such a mindset is that it falls into the category of logical fallacies known as *argumentum ad populum*—appeal to the majority (Archie, 2012). The variation of this fallacy known as "Bandwagon" is the idea in which someone attempts to "prove a conclusion on the grounds that all or most people think or believe it is true" (Archie). In other words, just because a lot of people believe in something (like macroevolution), that does not make it true—and the number of people who believe in it cannot be cited as evidence in support of the proposition. Just because bloodletting was "the most common procedure performed by surgeons for almost two thousand years," that should not have made it an acceptable idea, though it carried the weight of consensus behind it ("Bloodletting," 2012). Thankfully, a few brave scientists broke with the consensus view in pursuit of truth. Just because the consensus in medicine in the past, before Joseph Lister introduced the idea of sterile surgery (cf. "Joseph Lister...," 2013; Reynolds, 2009), was to not worry about cleanliness in operating rooms, that does not mean that such entrenched practices should not be questioned. Just because the consensus over millennia was that life could arise spontaneously from non-life (Balme, 1962)—a belief held even as late as 300 years ago when Francesco Redi conducted his experiments that began casting doubt on that idea—that does not mean that such a preposterous idea should have continued to exist. Just because the "consensus" in certain evolutionary circles only 100 years ago was that certain races should be considered inferior in the evolutionary chain (cf. Darwin, 1859; Stein and Miller, 2008), did that mean that everyone should have accepted the "consensus" and taken part in eliminating those deemed "weaker" or "less fit" by evolutionists?

"Majority rule" is hardly a suitable mindset for scientific investigation. Scientific breakthroughs are not made by the majority—but rather, by innovative individuals thinking outside the box, not thinking in

the same way as the majority. In fact, the "consensus" view is often times the very viewpoint that is wrong because of the "herd mentality" humanity tends to have. Just because there is a consensus in this country among the rank and file Americans that evolution is false (see Appendix 6.f), that should not be taken as evidence for or against evolution—whether or not the population is deemed "scientific" enough in the minds of the science community's self-promoting "credentials police." There exists an overwhelming consensus (92%) in the world that some kind of god(s) exists (cf. "Major Religions of the World...," 2007), and yet one can be assured that the atheistic evolutionary community would not want to appeal to the "consensus" argument in that case. Consider further: even if it is now the scientific consensus among the biology community that Darwinian evolution is true, what about **before** evolution had become consensus in that field? Should the "consensus rule" have been applied then, disallowing the spread of evolutionary theory? If so, then the biology community is in error for breaking its own rules and needs to go back to the old viewpoint in order to be consistent.

In truth, accepting the consensus view on a theory is a dangerous practice. Scientific theories are not "bad guys." Theories are important in order to make scientific progress. However, a theory (like the Theory of Evolution or the Big Bang Theory), by its very definition, is not known as **absolute**, but rather, as a **possible** explanation of something. A theory tacitly acknowledges the potential that it may be incorrect and that there may be other theories that fit the facts better, that may one day be proven as legitimate. This acknowledgement makes accepting the consensus view on a scientific theory a dangerous practice, since the theory may be wrong. A scientific law, however, is not based on "consensus" or speculation, but on the evidence—the facts. Therefore, there **should** be "consensus" about the laws of nature, even if there isn't. However, what makes those laws valid should not be, and is not, based on "consensus." The goal of science should be the pursuit of truth—not consensus; truth—not what's popular. That is what has and will lead to further scientific progress in this country and in the world.

The consensus in this country that has existed since its inception is that Creation is true and Darwinian evolution is false. The Christian would argue, in keeping with Scripture, that this consensus has no doubt played a role in the scientific breakthroughs that individual scientists have made that have significantly contributed to our nation's success. Such breakthroughs are to be expected according to the biblical model (Psalm 33:12). In this case, it is clear that following the "consensus" has been a good thing. The fact that Christianity was the "consensus," however, is not what made it true or false. It seems evident though, based on God's dealings with nations in the Bible, that He views the spiritual state of a nation by its consensus views on various matters, and He responds accordingly with blessings or punishments (Deuteronomy 11:13-17). In the past, it seems that God has providentially showered America with blessings—scientifically, economically, militarily, and in many other ways—in large part due to the "consensus" of Americans that believe the God of the Bible is the one true God and that the precepts of His Word make for a superior society (cf. Miller, D., 2008; Miller, 2009). Sadly, the consensus is changing, and in light of Scripture, we should expect God's blessings to diminish accordingly (Deuteronomy 7:12-16; 15:5-6; 28). May we encourage Christians always in your pursuit to boldly speak "the truth in love" (Ephesians 4:15), doing your part to make the American consensus one that believes in and seeks to obey the one true God of the Universe.

Review Questions

1) What logical fallacy illustrates the flawed reasoning of those who argue that one should accept something solely due to its being the "scientific" or "general" consensus?

2) Why is "majority rule" not a good idea in science?

3) Discuss scientific laws and theories as they relate to the idea of consensus.

"You Creationists are Unqualified to Speak about Evolution!"

A common quibble laid at the feet of the creationist is that he/she is not qualified to speak about scientific matters relating to the Creation/evolution controversy. For instance, recall Mark Isaak, who stated that "for every creationist who claims one thing, there are dozens of scientists (probably more), **all with far greater professional qualifications**, who say the opposite" (2005, emp. added). Others assert that creationists make "the elementary mistake of trying to discuss a highly specialized field...in which they have little or no training" (Holloway, 2010). Do these assertions have any merit?

First, such assertions are ironic in light of other statements by some in the evolutionary community. For example, in the "General Tips" section of the article, "How to Debate a Creationist," the *Creationism versus Science* Web site tells its followers:

> **[Y]ou don't need to become a qualified expert** [in relevant evolutionary subject matters—JM]...but you should endeavour to know as much or more about these subjects than your opponent does (which is often a surprisingly easy task, since most creationists learn only the barest superficialities of any given scientific principle before feeling confident enough to pontificate on it) (2007, parenthetical item in orig., emp. added).

It seems that some do not wish to hold all participants to the same standards. It is clear that the author wished for his audience to be able to win a debate, rather than consider the validity of the arguments being posed by creationists.

It is important to realize that when a person wishes to discuss a certain matter, it is not always necessary for the individual to have the relevant experience or credentials (as deemed necessary by the atheistic evolutionary community) in that area. Consider: Are certain qualifications needed before an individual can quote or paraphrase others who **are** considered "experts" on a certain matter, as do many creationists **and evolutionists** (especially in the media)? Does one need a B.A. degree in English before he would be considered qualified enough to be able to cite references? And would **that** degree be enough to prove qualification? Perhaps a **graduate level** degree in English would be necessary? Such a proposition would be preposterous. Even if a person had such qualifications, it would not guarantee that the person is credible, and it certainly would not prove that the person is infallible. The key, of course, is to determine whether or not the quotations and/or paraphrases are done correctly, regardless of who the commentator is. Granted, a person must have some level of knowledge to be able properly to engage in such practices, but a formal education in every area one wishes to discuss is simply unnecessary. Creationists and evolutionists, as well as individuals in every professional field, often cite others who are considered "experts." This is a reasonable and acceptable practice.

Follow this line of reasoning even further. How far are the evolutionists willing to go in their demand for credentials? Should scientists have **direct** experience in every field in which they make an assertion? If not, why not? If a biology professor's doctoral research dealt primarily with the characteristics of St. Augustine grass, is he/she qualified to speak about the evolution of apes and humans? If an atheist only received a B.A. degree in religion, would such a person be qualified to speak on the most notable, alleged, atheistic mechanism for the origin of man—namely the General Theory of Evolution? If not, then atheistic debater Dan Barker has no business speaking out about it and should be silenced (cf. Butt and Barker, 2009). **Even Charles Darwin, the "Father" of the General Theory of Evolution, only had a degree in theology**, having dropped out of the only other fields of formal education he at one time pursued—the medical and law

professions (Thompson, 1981, p. 104). Based on the standards being imposed by some in the evolutionary community, he had no business speaking out about matters pertaining to biology and should not have been taken seriously. And yet his free-lance work as a naturalist was considered substantial enough to gain him credibility upon writing *The Origin of Species*. We would argue that his qualifications were irrelevant. His ideas should be scrutinized to determine their worth, rather than castigating him for his lack of a science degree. However, in order to be consistent, the evolutionary community must deem him unqualified to discuss evolution, and his theory should be rejected. Consider further: should an atheist be required to have credentials in theology in order to be able to speak against God? Should an atheist have credentials in Bible matters to be able to speak against the Bible? A lack of "qualifications" in religious matters does not seem to stop rabid atheists from attacking Christianity. Clearly, a double-standard in the atheistic evolutionary community is at work.

And **how much** experience is required before a person can be considered qualified? Who defines where the imaginary line is that distinguishes between the "qualified" and the "unqualified"—whose thoughts and research should be considered and whose should be ignored? Who will be the qualifications policemen and what gives them such a right? Who determines what qualifications the qualifications policemen must have to be able to deem others qualified? And what credentials do those who ordain qualifications policemen need? If scientists were held to such standards, progress into new realms could never be made, since by definition, **there are no experts in such areas!** Thomas Edison received no higher education ("The Life of...," 1999), and yet he invented the light bulb, founded General Electric Company, and filed 1,093 successful U.S. patent applications for his inventions ("Edison's Patents," 2010). In 1997, the American Society of Mechanical Engineers saw fit to establish the "Thomas A. Edison Patent Award" in his honor, again, in spite of his lack of higher learning (McKivor, 2010). Sir Isaac Newton received a bachelor's degree, but without honors or distinction (Hatch, 2002). Should his work be disregarded? Consider also that his area of study was mathematics.

How was he qualified to discuss physics, mechanics, dynamics, and other mechanical engineering concepts that are taught in engineering schools today? The Wright brothers did not even receive high school diplomas, much less receive a college education (Kelly, 1989, p. 37). The *Encyclopedia of World Biography* notes that Henry Ford, founder of the Ford Motor Company, "was a poor student. He never learned to spell or to read well. Ford would write using only the simplest of sentences" ("Henry Ford," 2010). However, that did not stop people from buying his Model T. Nearly 15,500,000 were sold in the United States alone ("Henry Ford [1863-1947]," 2010). Jesus Christ, Himself, would not have had the credentials deemed necessary by the religious elites of His day to speak on theological matters. And yet, Jesus emphasized that truth is truth, regardless of one's credentials, and the truth will set men free (John 8:32). This is a foundational principle undergirding our entire education system (e.g., see the original seal of Harvard University, containing the Latin word, *veritas*, which, according to remarks by President Emeritus of Harvard Lawrence Summers, meant "divine truth" [2002]; John 8:32 is designated the "fundamental mission," "philosophical foundation," and the motto of the CIA [Central Intelligence Agency, 2012; Central Intelligence Agency, 2008].).

Another relevant point should be considered in this discussion as well. Creationists often speak about various fundamental, non-technical problems with evolution, such as the fact that life cannot come from non-life, the Universe must have a cause, nothing lasts forever or pops into existence spontaneously, and macroevolution does not happen. These beliefs, the creationist rightly contends, disprove atheistic evolution. The evolutionist often attempts to dodge these arguments by claiming that "creationists aren't qualified" to discuss these matters. But there is a fundamental problem with that assertion. Since no one has ever witnessed, much less been able to study, abiogenesis; or witnessed an effect without a cause; or witnessed kinds of creatures giving rise to other kinds of creatures (e.g., apes giving rise to humans); there is no such thing as being "qualified" in such areas. How can one be qualified to discuss things that do not happen? One person is

just as qualified as the next person to discuss such things. If someone has spent his entire life trying to find evidence that fairies fly around inside of children's eyeballs, all to no avail, does that mean that he is more qualified to discuss that matter than someone else? Of course not. All he has done is waste his time coming to the same conclusion everyone else had already arrived at. Everyone on Earth has the same relative amount of experience witnessing the fact that such things as abiogenesis and macroevolution do not happen. So any person is just as qualified as the next person to discuss them. Darwinian evolution is founded on principles for which there is no such thing as "being qualified" enough to discuss them. Conjecture and speculation—not proof—characterize evolutionary theory.

Bottom line: Anyone is eligible to take part in a discussion as long as he or she is not speaking error. **That** is the critical issue. Consider: does one have to be qualified to speak the truth? Of course not. Truth is truth! It does not matter who speaks it. Unfortunately, many critics of creationists fail to address the creationist's argument, but instead attack the speaker and his credentials. This assault sidesteps the argument and attempts to distract hearers from analyzing the argument's validity—a classic example of the *ad hominem* logical fallacy ("Fallacies," 2012). Anyone who is able to speak correctly concerning a scientific matter due to personal work or experience, direct study, or research into the work of others is eligible to take part in scientific discourse on the subject, given that the person is handling the matter accurately. As long as the laws of science are used correctly, anyone can teach their truths and should not be restricted from doing so through the silencing techniques being attempted by the evolutionary community.

As was mentioned earlier, some evolutionists assert that "there are dozens of scientists (probably more), all with far greater professional qualifications" than creationists (Isaak, 2005)—quite a bold statement, to say the least. It may be true that most scientists have bought into the hoax of evolution, as was the case when scientists believed in geocentricity, or that blood-letting was an appropriate prescription for curing ailments, but appealing to **numbers** proves nothing, and using such an argument causes one to fall victim to yet another logical fallacy—the *ad populum* fallacy (i.e., appeal to the majority) ("Fallacies," 2012). In the words of the seventeenth century Italian astronomer Galileo Galilei, considered by many to be the Father of Modern Science, "In questions of science, the authority of a thousand is not worth the humble reasoning of a single individual" (as quoted in "International Space Hall of Fame...," 2013; Arago, 1857).

Although numbers ultimately mean nothing in regard to truth, creationists can certainly come up with an impressive list of "qualified" scientists who have examined the scientific evidence and concluded that the atheistic evolutionary model falls short in explaining our existence. Johannes Kepler, the Father of Modern Astronomy and modern optics, was a firm Bible believer. Robert Boyle, the Father of Chemistry, was a Bible believer. Samuel F.B. Morse, who invented Morse Code, was a believer. Wernher Von Braun, the father of the space program at NASA, was a strong believer in God and Creation, as well as Louis Pasteur, the Father of Biology, Lord Kelvin, the Father of Thermodynamics, Sir Isaac Newton, the Father of Modern Physics, and Faraday, the Father of Electromagnetism. Dozens of other well-known scientists from history could be cited (see Morris, 1990). Were these men qualified scientists? If not, their work and the subsequent fields they fathered should be discarded. If they **were** qualified, should their positions on the Creation question be taken more seriously by the evolutionary community, simply because they were qualified in their eyes?

Creation Ministries International posted a list of some 187 scientists alive today (or recently deceased) who believe in the biblical account of Creation ("Creation Scientists...," 2010). The scientists who are listed all possess a doctorate in a science-related field. Over 90 different scientific fields are represented in the list, including several types of engineers, chemists, geneticists, physicists, and biologists. Astronomers and astrophysicists; geologists and geophysicists; physicians and surgeons; micro-, molecular, and neurobiologists; paleontologists and zoologists are represented, and the list goes on. Jerry Bergman amassed a list of some 3,000 individuals. Most have a Ph.D. in science, and many more could be added, according to Bergman:

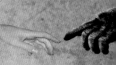
On my public list, I have close to 3,000 names, including about a dozen Nobel Prize winners but, unfortunately, a large number of persons that could be added to the public list, including many college professors, did not want their name listed because of real concerns over possible retaliation or harm to their careers (2012).

For over 30 years, we at Apologetics Press have conducted numerous seminars and published hundreds of articles by "qualified," credentialed scientists who speak out in support of the biblical account of Creation as well—scientists with graduate degrees in geology, astrophysics, microbiology, neurobiology, cell biology, medicine, biochemistry, aerospace engineering, nuclear engineering, and biomechanical engineering. Creationists can certainly speak with credibility in scientific matters. However, the ultimate question, once again, is not how many scientists are standing on either side of the battle line. Majority or "consensus" is not the deciding factor (see Appendix 6.a). The question is who is speaking **the truth**? Who is taking the scientific evidence and drawing reasonable, accurate conclusions from the facts? The answer is clear to the unbiased observer. Science supports **Creation**—not evolution.

There is certainly something to be said about the value of having credentials and experience in the area in which one is speaking, because that person will often have a broader perspective about a subject than the next person. But it is also true that that person should not be blindly accepted without critical thinking. Regardless of one's credentials, the audience must still consider the validity of the argument being offered. Those deemed legitimate by the "credentialed" community do not have a monopoly on knowledge or good ideas. Quite the contrary. When all is said and done, the theory—not the person discussing it—should be where the emphasis lies. As always, we challenge the audience to disprove our contentions. Truth will always win. It will set us free.

Review Questions

1) What behavior illustrates the self-contradiction of those that argue that "creationists aren't qualified to discuss scientific matters"?

2) What points illustrate the fact that it is not always necessary for an individual to have the relevant experience or credentials (as deemed necessary by the atheistic evolutionary community) in the area in which he is speaking or writing?

3) What is the critical factor that determines whether someone is eligible to take part in a discussion?

4) When a person attacks the speaker instead of the argument, what logical fallacy is he guilty of making?

5) When a person cites the number of individuals that supports his belief, rather than offering logical argumentation for the belief, he is guilty of what fallacy?

6) Name some of the pioneers of science that were creationists.

"Science Only Involves Natural— Not Supernatural—Events."

When thoroughly scrutinized, error always exposes itself through some kind of self-contradiction. Truth alone stands the test of scrutiny. One such example is highlighted when considering a fundamental plank of the atheistic naturalist's position.

The atheist says, "I refuse to consider believing in anything that isn't natural—whose explanation cannot be found in nature. Everything must and can be explained through natural processes." So, according to the atheist, the existence of everything in the Universe must be explainable by natural means—nothing unnatural (e.g., a supernatural Being) can be considered in the equation. Robert Hazen, in his lecture series, *Origins of Life*, said:

> In this lecture series I make a basic **assumption** that life emerged by some kind of **natural process**. I propose that life arose by a sequence of events that are completely consistent with the **natural laws** of chemistry and physics. **In this assumption I am like most other scientists** [i.e., naturalistic scientists—JM]. I believe in a universe that is ordered by these **natural laws**. Like other scientists, I rely on the power of **observations and experiments** and theoretical reasoning to understand how the cosmos came to be the way it is (2005, emp. added).

According to the National Academy of Sciences:

> One goal of science is to understand **nature**.... The statements of science must invoke only **natural things and processes**. The statements of science are those that emerge from the application of human intelligence to data obtained from **observation and experiment**.... Progress in science consists of the development of better explanations

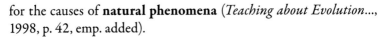

for the causes of **natural phenomena** (*Teaching about Evolution...*, 1998, p. 42, emp. added).

The problem is that in holding this position, the naturalist quickly runs into walls of scientific fact that contradict it. As has been discussed, the laws of science are formal declarations of what have been proven, time and again through science, to occur **in nature** without exception. The naturalist cannot hold a view that contradicts the laws of nature without simultaneously contradicting his purely naturalistic position. But this is precisely the position that the naturalist is in.

> The naturalist cannot hold a view that contradicts the laws of nature without simultaneously contradicting himself.

The naturalist must allege an explanation not in keeping with nature for many things we find in the Universe. For example, the naturalist's explanation of the origin of matter and energy (i.e., spontaneous generation or eternal existence) is unnatural (i.e., in contradiction to the First and Second Laws of Thermodynamics; see chapter two). The naturalist must further contradict himself by alleging an unnatural explanation for the origin of life (i.e., abiogenesis, in contradiction to the Law of Biogenesis; see chapters five through seven). And what's more, the naturalist must contradict himself by alleging that various kinds of living creatures can give rise to other kinds of living creatures through macroevolution—a contention which, unlike microevolution, has never been observed to occur in nature (see chapters seven and eight and Thompson, et al., 2002). Abiogenesis, spontaneous energy generation, the eternality of matter, and macroevolution are all **unnatural** suggestions since they have never been **observed** to occur in nature, and yet they are fundamental to the naturalist's unnatural view. Simply put, the atheistic naturalist's position is self-contradictory.

The worldview that **is** in keeping with the evidence—that is not self-contradictory—is the Christian faith as described in the pages of the Bible. The naturalist cannot explain the Universe without relying on unnatural means. The creationist has no problem with non-natural explanations, since the Bible clearly states that God—a supernatural

Being—created the Universe and life. Truth is never self-contradictory. When scrutinized, it always comes out on top. When a person chooses to fight it, he will inevitably get hurt in the end. "The fool has said in his heart, 'There is no God'" (Psalm 53:1).

Science vs. Evolution

Review Questions

1) What can a naturalist not contradict without being guilty of self-contradiction?

2) Name specific examples that illustrate the naturalist's self-contradiction.

242

Appendix 6.d

"Science and God/Religion are Incompatible."

Some contend that science is at odds with religion. They suggest that the scientific method requires empirical testing, but God's existence cannot be empirically verified. Science supposedly proves the Big Bang, evolutionary theory, an ancient Universe, and dinosaurs that never co-existed with humans, while the Bible mistakenly contends that the Universe was created in six literal, 24-hour days only a few thousand years ago, with humans and dinosaurs being created together on day six. Supposedly, science is based on verifiable evidence, whereas religion is based on "blind faith" and ambiguous "tinglies" attributed to the Holy Spirit. For such reasons, it is claimed that science and Scripture cannot be harmonized—that they are diametrically opposed to each other. Are such accusations legitimate?

In reality, however, true science agrees perfectly with Scripture. Though God's existence cannot be empirically verified, it can be easily verified through inductive reasoning from the scientific evidence available to us—in the same way forensic scientists use science to investigate events that they did not personally witness. Origin-of-life biologist Stephen Meyer reasoned, "A pattern of flowers spelling 'Welcome to Disneyland' allows visitors to the theme park to detect intelligent activity, even if they did not see the flowers planted or arranged. Similarly, the specified and complex arrangement of nucleotide sequences—the information—in DNA implies the past action and existence of an intelligent cause, even if the past action of the cause cannot directly be observed" (2009, Ch. 15).

As we have seen in this book, abundant scientific evidence exists which refutes naturalistic evolutionary theory. Other evidence also shows that the Universe, in keeping with the Creation model, is not as old as evolutionists allege (e.g., DeYoung, 2005), and still other evidence proves that dinosaurs and humans co-existed (e.g., Lyons and Butt, 2008). The concept of "blind faith," though championed by many who call themselves Christians, is at odds with Scripture, which defines "faith" as choosing to believe in something, **based on the evidence that has been presented for it**, and responding accordingly (see Appendix 6.e). Atheistic scientists might hope to burn the bridge between science and true religion, but such pursuits are vain.

When handled accurately (2 Timothy 2:15), Scripture and science complement each other perfectly. For instance, as we have mentioned several times, science has shown us that matter is not eternal, according to the Second Law of Thermodynamics (see chapter two), and could not have spontaneously generated, according to the First Law of Thermodynamics (see chapter two). This fact indicates that matter must have been placed here by an Entity outside the physical Universe. This truth, arrived at through science and inductive reasoning, is **not in harmony** with atheism and much of today's pseudo-science. But this truth **is** in keeping with the Bible, which says in its very first verse that God—a Being not subject to the laws of nature (i.e., a supernatural Being)—created the heavens and the Earth. Science supports Scripture.

Science has shown us that in nature, life comes only from life and that of its kind, according to the Law of Biogenesis (see chapters five through seven). Again, this fact indicates that a Being outside of nature must exist Who initiated life. This truth, arrived at through science and inductive reasoning, is **not in harmony** with atheism and much of today's pseudoscientific world which must contend, without scientific support, that life popped into existence from non-life. Rather, this truth **is** in keeping with the Bible, which says in Genesis 1:11, 24, and 2:7 that God created life. Science supports Scripture.

Science—the Law of Biogenesis and the rules of genetic reproduction—has shown us that living beings produce other living beings

of their own kind (see chapters seven and eight). There may be small changes along the way (e.g., in beak size, color, body size, etc.), but the offspring of a bird is still a bird. The offspring of a fish is still a fish. Therefore, since there is no common ancestor for all living beings from which all species evolved, there must be a supernatural Being Who initially created various kinds of life on Earth. This truth, arrived at through science and inductive reasoning, is **not in harmony** with the teachings of atheism and much of today's pseudo-scientific world, which argues that various kinds of living beings can give rise to completely different kinds of living beings. But this truth **is** in keeping with the Bible, which says in Genesis 1:21 and 1:24-25 that God directed living beings to reproduce after their kind. Science supports Scripture.

True science is in harmony with true religion. Why would science lie? It does not have a mind of its own. It has no bias or agenda. It can certainly be misrepresented or its findings misinterpreted, but science is not the enemy of true religion. In fact, according to the Bible, God, Himself, instituted the field of science. When God created human beings on day six and told them to "have dominion" over the Earth and "subdue" it (Genesis 1:28), He was commanding mankind to do something that would require extensive scientific investigation and experimentation. If God founded science, why would science be at odds with religion? When God, through His servant Paul, said in Romans 1:20 that His existence and some of His attributes could be learned from His creation, He was putting His stamp of approval on the scientific study of creation. When He said in 1 Thessalonians 5:21 to "[t]est all things; hold fast what is good," He was essentially summarizing the scientific method. Bottom line: God founded science. When legitimate scientific findings are interpreted properly and fairly, science supports the Bible and Christianity. It certainly is not at odds with the Bible.

Science vs. Evolution

Review Questions

1) Although God cannot be empirically observed, why is it not necessarily a "blind faith" to believe in Him?
2) What are some examples that show how science is in keeping with the Creation model?

"Unlike Evolutionists, Creationists Have a Blind, Evidence-less Faith!"

We openly grant that the accusation represented by the title of this appendix is true, at least for many individuals today. But not for all.

"Blind Faith"—Many Have It

What is "blind faith"? What is meant by that accusation? The idea behind "blind faith" is that a person chooses to believe in something or someone (namely, God) without any supporting evidence. The portrait painted in our minds is that of a person who puts on a blindfold and steps up to a ledge. He cannot see what is beyond the ledge. He has no idea how far down the drop is—whether or not he will plummet to his death, break his legs, or simply fall down. He has no idea if there is water, a trampoline, or rocks at the bottom. He simply decides to believe that he will not die if he jumps off—that he will be safe. He has no evidence, only pure, baseless "faith." So, he takes a "leap of faith." Question: who in their right mind would do such a thing? Whoever has such a "faith" truly is naïve, an extremely emotionally, rather than rationally, charged individual, and possibly is in need of counseling, or has an agenda for doing so.

Sadly, many people have such a "faith." Many people call themselves Christians, and claim to believe in the Bible, but clearly have not read it. They have a "blind faith" which, based on the Law of Rationality (see the Introduction), is irrational. Their belief in God is not based on the evidence, but is a blind leap into the dark without it. However, the biblical portrait of faith (Greek, *pistis*—translated equally as faith, belief, trust, or having confidence in; Arndt, et al., 1979, pp. 661-664) is not what some in Christendom have defined it to be, nor what Hollywood has portrayed it to be. It is not "believing when common sense tells you not to," as the 1947 movie, *Miracle on 34th Street* suggested (Seaton). It is not a "leap of faith" like Dr. Jones' actions in *Indiana Jones and the Last Crusade* (Spielberg, 1989). Contrary to what some "Christians" allege, the Bible does not advocate a "Feel, don't think" mentality, like that encouraged by Qui-Gon Jinn in *Star Wars* (Lucas, 1999). Biblical faith is based on evidence (Hebrews 11:1). It is trust—like the trust one has in a parent or friend—that is based on proof. We trust someone when he has proven himself to be trustworthy. When one listens to or reads revelation from God's Word (i.e., what Bible believers call "special revelation") and the information therein proves to be true, one develops faith in God (Romans 10:17). When one examines the evidence from the created order (i.e., what Bible believers call "general revelation"), and it points to the existence of a supernatural Being as Creator—rather than blind, random, accidental change over time—we learn to trust in the existence of God based on that evidence (Romans 1:20).

In short: The biblical model of faith requires **evidence**. According to the biblical model, the truth of God can be **known**—not felt or accepted without proof—and it will set men free (John 8:32). Sincere truth seekers examine what they have been told and investigate its veracity by pondering the evidence, as did the "fair-minded" Bereans of Acts 17:11 before becoming Christians. In fact, God (through Paul in 1 Thessalonians 5:21) tells the creationist that he is **expected** to prove or test something before believing it—only accepting what has been proven right or good. Do such passages give the impression that the Bible advocates a blind, evidence-less faith?

Sadly, evidence-based faith is not the faith of many within Christendom. But "don't throw the baby out with the bathwater." Many of us base our view **squarely on the evidence**. [NOTE: See Miller, 2003; Miller 2011a; and Miller, 2011b for more on the topics of "blind faith," logic, rationality, and the Bible.]

But We Don't

In order for a belief to not be "blind" or irrational, it needs supporting evidence. While the creationist does not claim to hold direct, observable evidence of God, since we cannot taste, touch, see, hear, or smell Him, the indirect evidence—a legitimate source of scientific evidence—is overwhelming. What supporting evidence do creationists put forth? A thorough treatment of this subject is outside the scope of this book, but hundreds of articles and books deal eloquently and credibly with the subject. [NOTE: See www.apologeticpress.org for a library of said material.]

In short, the creationist argues, among other things, that:

1) As discussed throughout this book, the available evidence contradicts the atheistic model, which logically leaves theism—the Creation model;

2) The fundamental evidence that contradicts the naturalistic model, supports the contentions of the Creation model, which never contradicts the scientific evidence;

3) The existence and teachings of the laws of science demand a non-material, uncaused Cause for the Universe;

4) There are numerous natural evidences in the Universe that exhibit the characteristics of intent, purpose, and complexity, which indicate a Mind behind them. Such attributes testify to the presence of intelligent **design**, which implies a **Designer**;

5) Objective morality exists, which implies a higher Law that transcends mankind, which in turn demands a supernatural Author;

6) A Book exists that contains certain characteristics that can only be explainable if it is what it says it is—the Word of the Creator.

These proofs, and many others, provide evidence that demands an explanation and cannot be satiated by naturalistic theories. Only supernatural creation provides an answer in keeping with the evidence. The Creation model can hardly be deemed unscientific. Its legitimate followers cannot be brushed aside as "blind" believers. Such sweeping accusations are unfair and betray a prejudiced, stereotypical mindset, to say nothing of the fact that such accusations fall victim to the *ad hominem* logical fallacy ("Fallacies," 2012).

Actually, *Evolutionists* Do.

In truth, Creation is the reasonable choice—the one not beholden to evidence-less leaps of faith. It is not contingent on the baseless, mythical claim that aliens exist and initiated life on Earth; that abiogenesis—like magic from a fictional novel—is somehow possible; that non-humans give birth to humans, as they do in the tabloids; or the fanciful idea that Universes spontaneously pop into existence. Indeed, atheistic evolution is simply well-packaged superstition. Creation is the option in keeping with reason and the evidence.

> Evolution is simply well-packaged superstition.

While some who call themselves "Christians" sadly do have an unscriptural, blind faith, in truth, as we have shown in this book, the same can be said of the evolutionary community—and more so. Why? (1) Because unlike evolution, the evidence does not contradict Creation but supports it, even though some have accepted Creation without that evidence; (2) because not **all** creationists hold to a blind faith. Some examine the evidence and draw the reasonable conclusion that a Creator exists. However, **all naturalists must** have a blind, evidence-less faith, since atheistic evolution is based on certain baseless, unprovable assumptions, including abiogenesis, naturalism, spontaneous generation or eternality of matter, etc. (cf. Miller, 2013 and Kerkut, 1960 for other key, baseless evolutionary assumptions). Belief in those assumptions is purely **blind**. As has been shown in previous chapters, they (1) are not supported by the evidence, which classifies evolution as irrational; (2) actually contradict the evidence; and (3) even show the naturalist to be engaged in self-contradiction, which he blindly ignores when confronted with the evidence of his contradictions (see Appendix 6.c). It seems clear that it is the evolutionist—not the creationist—who holds to a blind faith.

Recall the following timeless quotes from various prominent evolutionists [NOTE: As is the trend in the scientific community, the following scientists erroneously use the terms "science," "scientists," "scientific," etc. as synonomous with **naturalistic** science—as though they are one and the same, and as though **all** scientists are naturalists and have the same problems they have run into in their studies.]:

- Robert Jastrow: "At present, science has no satisfactory answer to the question of the origin of life on the earth. Perhaps the appearance of life on the earth is a **miracle**. Scientists are reluctant to accept that view, but their choices are limited; either life was created on the earth by the will of a being outside the grasp of scientific understanding, or it evolved on our planet spontaneously, through chemical reactions occurring in nonliving matter lying on the surface of the planet. The first theory places the question of the origin of life beyond the reach of scientific inquiry. It is a statement of faith in the power of a Supreme Being not subject to the laws of science. The second theory is **also an act of faith**. The act of faith consists in **assuming** that the scientific view of the origin of life is correct, **without having concrete evidence to support that belief**" (1977, pp. 62-63, emp. added).

- The late John Sullivan, a popular evolutionary science writer: "The hypothesis that life has developed from inorganic matter is, at present, still an **article of faith**" (1933, p. 95, emp. added).

- G.A. Kerkut, British evolutionary physiologist: The spontaneous generation of life is "**a matter of faith** on the part of the biologist.... The evidence for what did happen is **not available**" (1960, p. 150, emp. added).

- Loren Eiseley, evolutionary anthropologist of the University of Pennsylvania: "With the failure of these many efforts, science was left in the somewhat embarrassing position of having to postulate theories of living origins which it could not demonstrate. After having chided the theologian for his reliance on myth and miracle, science found itself in the unenviable position of having to create a **mythology of its own**: namely, the **assumption** that what, after long effort, could not be proved to take place today, had, in truth, taken place in the primeval past" (1957, pp. 201-202, emp. added).

251

- Fred Hoyle and Chandra Wickramasinghe: "It is doubtful that anything like the conditions which were simulated in the laboratory existed at all on a primitive Earth, or occurred for long enough times and over sufficiently extended regions of the Earth's surface to produce large enough local concentrations of the biochemicals required for the start of life. In accepting the 'primeval soup theory' of the origin of life, scientists have replaced **religious mysteries** which shrouded this question with **equally mysterious scientific dogmas**. The implied scientific dogmas are **just as inaccessible to the empirical approach**" (1978, p. 26, emp. added).

- Richard Lewontin, evolutionary geneticist of Harvard University: "Our willingness to accept scientific claims **against common sense** is the key to an understanding of the real struggle between science and the supernatural. We take the side of science **in spite** of the **patent absurdity** of some of its constructs..., **in spite** of the tolerance of the scientific community for **unsubstantiated just-so stories**, because we have a prior commitment, **a commitment to naturalism**. It is not that the methods and institutions of science somehow compel us to accept a material explanation of the phenomenal world, but, on the contrary, that **we are forced by our *a priori* adherence to material causes** to create an apparatus of investigation and a set of concepts that produce material explanations, no matter how **counter-intuitive**, no matter how **mystifying** to the uninitiated. Moreover, **that materialism is absolute, for we cannot allow a Divine Foot in the door**" (1997, p. 31, 2nd and 4th emp. in orig.).

- Robert Hazen: "I make an **assumption** that life emerged from basic raw materials through a sequence of events that was completely consistent with the natural laws of chemistry and physics. Even with this scientific approach, there is a possibility that we'll never know—in fact, that we can't ever know. It is possible that life emerged by an almost **infinitely improbable** sequence of difficult chemical reactions. If life is the result of an **infinitely improbable** succession of chemical steps, then any scientific attempt to understand life's origin is **doomed to failure**; such a succession **could not be duplicated** in a program of lab experiments. If the origin of life was an **infinitely improbable** accident, then there's absolutely **nothing** you or I or anyone else could do to figure out how it happened. I must tell you, that's a depressing thought to

someone like me who has devoted a decade to understanding the origin of life" (2005, emp. added).

- Boyce Rensberger, evolutionary science writer and director of the Knight Fellowship at M.I.T.: "At this point, it is necessary to reveal a little inside information about how scientists work, something the textbooks don't usually tell you. The fact is that scientists are **not really as objective and dispassionate** in their work as they would like you to think. Most scientists first get their ideas about how the world works not through rigorously logical processes but through **hunches and wild guesses.** As individuals they often come to believe something to be true long **before they assemble the hard evidence** that will convince somebody else that it is. **Motivated by faith** in his own ideas and **a desire for acceptance** by his peers, a scientist will labor for years knowing in his heart that his theory is correct but devising experiment after experiment whose results he **hopes** will support his position" (1986, pp. 17-18, emp. added).

If these quotes from eminent evolutionists do not prove that naturalistic evolution is a religious faith, and a **blind** one at that, what would? It's no wonder that the late Colin Patterson, senior paleontologist at the British Museum of Natural History in London, said about evolution, "One morning I woke up and something had happened in the night, and it struck me that I had been working on this stuff for twenty years and there was **not one thing I knew about it**. That's quite a shock to learn that one can be misled so long. Either there was something wrong with me, or there was something wrong with evolutionary theory" (1981, emp. added). These quotes simply do not characterize true Christianity or the true Creation model—but they **do** characterize evolution.

Thus, it seems that the rank and file evolutionist's self-incriminating, venomous accusations towards the creationist are represented well by the Shakespearean quote, "The lady doth protest too much, methinks" (2011, III.2). Be wary of the one who makes the loudest accusations and attempts to divert attention from his own inadequacies.

Bottom line: The true model of origins will be based on the evidence. It will be the rational model. It will not contradict the evidence at every turn. So evolution is not the true model of origins.

Science vs. Evolution

Review Questions

1) What is meant by the words "blind faith"?

2) Is it true that some "Christians" have a blind faith?

3) Does the Bible endorse one having "blind faith"? Discuss the passages that apply.

4) What **kind** of evidence points to the existence of God?

5) List various evidences that point to the existence of God.

6) Why is belief in naturalistic evolution a "blind faith"?

"Why are You Even Fighting Evolution, Anyway? Why would it Hurt the Creationist to Just Believe it?"

So what? Why is it important to spend time writing a book discussing evolutionary theory? What's the big deal? Isn't this whole discussion a waste of time? What if evolution **is** true? Why should that bother creationists? Does it really matter? In short, yes, there are important reasons to consider the validity of evolutionary theories.

To the Atheist

The Value of Truth

Is **truth** really that important? Would it be better to believe a lie that will make us feel good now, for a short period of time, but will destroy our lives in the future? Or is it better to know the truth? The answer to that question is pivotal, whether you are an atheist or theist. Would it be better to believe a lie that, "Cocaine must be good, because it makes a person feel good now"? Or would it be better to know the truth: that cocaine will destroy you, your family, and your future? One must ask himself, "Do I want to know the truth?" Do you want to know the truth about naturalism and its deadly effects?

Who would argue that searching for the truth is **not** important— that blindly accepting a false idea or a lie would be a good thing? Who would argue that ignoring truth due to its inconvenience, or its opposition to our personal desires, and engaging in self-delusion, are healthy, sensible practices? Surely, no one would—at least not consciously. Humans have an inner drive for the truth, especially concerning those matters that are of such import in our lives that they could affect our physical lives and eternal destiny. Those who bury their heads in the sand and apathetically ignore the debate on this crucial subject—belittling it as unimportant—are living in a dream world, and a dangerous one at that.

Cosmic evolution is the only conceivable explanation for the Universe available to the atheist. If evolution is false, Creation is true, and therefore, the existence of God stands as the only option in keeping with the evidence. [NOTE: It is not within the scope of this book to show how, after arriving at the existence of a god, one can proceed to arrive at the existence of the God of the Bible as the one true God, the fact that the Bible is His inspired Word, and therefore, that the Bible's Creation model is the true account of the origin of the Universe. However, this matter is addressed elsewhere. See www.apologeticspress.org.] If God exists, one must live as He stipulates in order to receive eternal life and avoid eternal punishment. If the Bible is true, then obedience to it will lead—not to passing, momentary pleasure (Hebrews 11:24-26)—but to deep, long-lasting happiness and peace, regardless of the things that happen to us in life (cf. Proverbs 29:18; Deuteronomy 6:24; 10:12-13; Psalm 19:7-8; Philippians 4:6-7; Matthew 6:25-34; Proverbs 3:5-6; James 1:2-3; Hebrews 12:5-11; Revelation 21:4). Who would reject such an offer? If it is true, why would someone not wish to know it? I plead with you to consider this crucial point, because the alternative is also spoken of in the Bible.

If evolution is false, and the God of the Bible exists, there will be eternal punishment for those who choose to ignore His Word (2 Thessalonians 1:6-10). He will not force anyone to obey Him. It is not in the nature of love to do so, and the God of the Bible proclaims Himself to be Love (1 John 4:7-8). It is our decision whether or not we choose to go to heaven. Most will not (Matthew 7:13-14), but it is not God's will that such occur. He desires repentance (2 Peter 3:9), but He will not force us, else we become robots without freewill.

Freedom is one of the loving gifts the God of the Bible has bestowed on mankind—the ability to choose our destiny.

Naturalism: A Scary Picture

There is no such thing as a purely naturalistic society. Theists who are governed by the moral codes of their religion permeate the Earth, comprising at least 92% of the population ("Major Religions of the World...," 2007). Many naturalists in America today, however, wish to eliminate theism from society—from schools and from the public square. Belief in God is an unscientific, unenlightened concept that should be eliminated, in their minds, and replaced with naturalism and its evolutionary theories. But is this really a good idea, even from a naturalist's perspective?

What would we expect a purely naturalistic society to look like? If there is no higher Power, then "anything goes." In the words of atheistic philosopher Jean Paul Sartre, "Everything is indeed permitted if God does not exist.... [H]e cannot find anything to depend upon within or outside himself" (1989). This truth is common sense. If you have no higher Power in the back of your mind—One that has supreme control of your eternal destiny, encouraging you to behave decently and unselfishly towards others, why would you bother, if you could get away with it? If you wanted to do something terrible or take something that is not yours, you had the ability to do it without being caught, and you could justify it in your mind, what would keep you from doing it if it were in your best interest? In a purely naturalistic society, controlling oneself for "the greater good" would hardly be a strong enough motivation to keep one in check when one is hungry, poor, angry, or passionately wants something that is not his, especially if he could legitimize his decision in his own mind and before others as merely the result of his animalistic evolutionary instincts. After all, in a naturalistic society, animalism is not discouraged (and even tacitly encouraged), considering that animals are our ancestors and that we are animals, ourselves, under the naturalistic mindset.

Even if "the greater good" were a strong enough motivator for some, who would define what would be better for the greater good? Would not that person become god-like? Could that individual be counted on to act in the best interest of the entire society? And if each individual were left to himself to decide what would be for "the greater good," then is it not true that chaos would reign? What one person believes would be better for others would not necessarily agree with the next person's view. Our prisons are full to over-flowing with evidence of this fact. Would we not expect to see even more chaos if a high percentage of society did not subscribe to a higher belief system than themselves? "I believe that if I have your car, I would be able to do more good for other people. I'm stronger than you, and have more powerful friends, so I'm taking it." "I believe that if your wife were communal property for everyone to use, that would be better for society. The majority agrees with me. So move out of our way." "It was okay for me to shoot my neighbor. The ends justify the means, after all. I did society a service. His music drives everybody crazy." Under the naturalistic system, "might makes right." The strong—the "fittest"—will survive. Can you imagine such a society? Would you want to live in such a society? If not, why try to create it by taking part in the attempt to remove God from this one? [NOTE: See Butt, 2008b and Lyons, 2011 for a study of the dangerous societal implications of naturalism.]

In such a naturalistic society, one's behavioral decisions would ultimately come down to how insightful, wise, discerning, knowledgeable, and understanding that person is about how his/her behaviors would affect others. Would you wish to entrust your life, possessions, and family to the wisdom—or lack thereof—of those you see in society today? Imagine the decisions that younger, less experienced, less knowledgeable individuals in society would make, even in the name of helping the "greater good." Yet their behavior would certainly have a significant effect on society, since their youthful strength and hormones could make them capable of terrible things. Without God—an overriding Power Whose Law supersedes personal opinion; Whose love generates trust; Whose omniscience generates truth; Whose omnipotence generates fear—a society would be dark indeed. That makes this discussion of critical importance. If evolution is found to be untenable, naturalism falls with it—and it is critical that naturalism falls.

 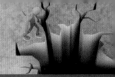

To the Christian

A Recent Gallup Poll

What about theistic evolution? Could not God have created the Universe using evolutionary theories (e.g., Big Bang cosmology and Darwinian evolution), filling in the gaps that have been highlighted in this book? Does it really matter? If the Bible could be interpreted in such a way that evolutionary theory could fit into its Creation model, why not do so? If evolution and theism can be reconciled, why fight it? Would such a practice really bring about any harm to the Christian worldview? These are relevant, reasonable questions that many in the religious and non-religious world are asking. While a thorough study of the various prominent theistic evolutionary theories is outside the scope of this book (see Thompson, 2000 for such a study), since this book is based on the assertion and assumption that theistic evolution is not an option for the Christian, and since belief in the doctrine could have eternal implications, an introduction to the subject is worthwhile.

According to a Gallup poll released in June of 2012, the percentage of Americans who hold to the creationist view on the matter of origins, as opposed to the evolutionary view, remained constant over the last 30 years (Newport, 2012). Nearly half (46%) of Americans believe that God created human beings "pretty much in their present form at one time within the last 10,000 years or so" (Newport). Amazingly, in spite of decades of incessant bombardment on the minds of young people in public schools by the evolutionary community, Darwinian evolution is making no headway in swaying biblical creationists.

The pollsters highlighted a sobering connection between how "religious" a person is and their likelihood of being a creationist versus an evolutionist. According to the poll, "the **most religious** Americans are most likely to be creationists" (2012, emp. added). Of those who attend worship **each** week, 25% believe in theistic evolution and 67% believe in the creation of the Universe within the last 10,000 years. For those who attend **almost** every week or month, 31% believe in theistic evolution and 55% believe in creationism. Of those who attend **seldom** or **never**, 38% believe in theistic evolution and only 25% believe in creationism (2012). The implication is that the less religious a person becomes, moving away from a consistent contemplation of spiritual matters (i.e., the worship of God and a study of His Word), the more he will capitulate to the prevailing secular viewpoint instead of the biblical viewpoint.

One unfortunate finding from the Gallup poll was that the percentage of those who believe in theistic evolution, in one form or another, appears to have gradually declined over the years (from 38% to 32%), while the percentage of those who believe in secular evolution has increased by the same amount (from 9% to 15%) (2012). That's 19,000,000 Americans! This finding supports the contention that theistic evolution is a gateway doctrine that leads many to reject God and the Bible altogether—which is a major reason why Apologetics Press has long sought to fight the spread of this debilitating doctrine.

Darwinian evolution is not a belief that comes from a straightforward reading of the Bible. It is a theory that is championed by the secular world and that many religious people have felt pressure to accept. Many feel the need to attempt to squeeze Darwinian evolution into the text of Genesis chapter one, in spite of its clear teaching that the Universe was spoken into existence in six, approximately 24-hour days. This practice can be devastating in the long run, destroying one's faith in the Bible and Christianity and giving ammunition to the Bible's skeptics. How so?

Theistic Evolution—A Devastating Doctrine

Genesis One: Figurative and Symbolic?

The theistic evolutionist often tries to evade the clarity of the Genesis account of Creation by contending that it is not a literal, historical account, but rather is figurative and symbolic. In other words, Genesis chapter one does not actually mean what it says. The days mentioned, for instance, may not have been literal days. The Bible certainly uses figurative language at times (e.g., in the Psalms, Revelation, Daniel, etc.). However, the fact that we can **know** that such language is being used, proves that there are textual indicators that distinguish historical from figurative and symbolic genres of writing in the Bible.

For example, when Genesis 25 describes Esau's appearance as being "like a hairy garment all over," we understand that his skin was not literally a hairy garment. Rather, it was similar to the appearance and feel of a hairy garment. When the 23rd Psalm says that the Lord "makes me to lie down in green pastures" and "leads me beside the still waters," we understand that the text is not speaking literally, but figuratively. In Daniel chapter two, Daniel interpreted King Nebuchadnezzar's dream, which depicted a "great image" with a head of gold, chest and arms of silver, belly and thighs of bronze, legs of iron, and its feet composed of iron and clay. Daniel said to Nebuchadnezzar, "You are the head of gold" (vs. 38). We, of course, understand that Daniel was not speaking literally. He was explaining that the gold head of the image was symbolic and represented the greatness of Nebuchadnezzar's Babylonian empire in comparison to the lesser kingdoms that would follow his. We can know that Revelation is a book that is to be taken figuratively and symbolically, because John tells us so right at the beginning of the book (i.e., Revelation 1:1—"And He sent and **sign**ified it...." Revelation is a book filled with signs and apocalyptic language, intended to be taken figuratively [cf. Arndt, et al., 1979, p. 92]).

Similarly, one can readily distinguish the difference between a heavily symbolic account of Creation, like that given in Psalm 104, and the account given in Genesis one—which is given in straight-forward, narrative terminology. Genesis one gives every indication of being a historical account of Creation. [NOTE: Biblical Hebrew scholar, Steven Boyd, in the book *Thousands...Not Billions*, engaged in a fascinating study, where he showed, using a statistical analysis of verb uses in 97 poetic and narrative biblical texts, that Genesis 1:1-2:3 unquestionably belongs in the category of narrative texts (DeYoung, 2005, pp. 157-170).]

That said, if a text like Genesis one, that has no indication that it is anything other than a literal, historical narrative, is taken to be figurative, as the theistic evolutionary proposition requires, then (1) the biblical account of Creation is at best misleading and at worst, deceptive—either of which would categorize the Bible as uninspired; and (2) what would keep a person from calling anything and everything

else in the Bible symbolic as well? How can we know for certain that Jesus was really born of a virgin, was crucified, and was resurrected? What would prohibit such accounts from being interpreted as figurative and symbolic as well? Some have gone so far! When the Bible tells us things that we should or should not do to be pleasing to God, what would keep us from interpreting those areas of Scripture as figurative as well? Interpreting Genesis one as figurative has far reaching implications.

In truth, one can come to know what in the Bible is figurative and what is not. When the evidence from the biblical text is weighed (cf. Thompson, 2000), it is clear that Genesis one relates a literal account of Creation in six, approximately 24-hour days, within the last 10,000 years. The scientific evidence supports this contention, as we point out on a regular basis at Apologetics Press. However, such issues highlight how critical the question of origins is, as it is fundamental to our interpretation of Scripture. Reading things into the biblical text that are not warranted can be a very slippery slope. Such practices are just as forbidden as adding man-made doctrines and practices into the church of the Bible (cf. Matthew 15:8-9; Colossians 3:17; 1 Corinthians 4:6; John 4:24; Revelation 22:18-19; Galatians 1:8-9).

Inspired Mistakes?

Consider further, if theistic evolution is true, then Moses was in error in his writings and was, therefore, not inspired by God. Moses clearly stated in Exodus 20:11 that everything—"the heavens and the earth, the sea, and all that is in them"—was made in six days. When the plural form of the Hebrew word for "day" (*yamim*) is used in Old Testament non-prophetic literature, like Exodus 20:11, it always refers to literal 24-hour periods of time. The same can be said when this Hebrew word is preceded by a numeral, as in Exodus 20:11 (cf. Thompson, 2000, pp. 188-201). Why? Because it would make no sense to speak of six "long periods of time." So, according to Moses, the entire Universe, with everything in it, was created in six, literal, 24-hour periods of time. If theistic evolution were true, then Moses' writings—a significant section of our Bibles—would be in error, and the skeptic would be accurate in concluding that Moses was not inspired

by God. And further, any other biblical characters who quoted from Moses' writings as though he was an inspired author (including Jesus, Himself—Matthew 4:4,7,10), would also be in error.

If theistic evolution were true, Paul also would be in error. Speaking of mankind, Paul said in Romans 1:20 that certain attributes of God have been "clearly perceived" by mankind "ever since the creation of the world" (ESV). If theistic evolution is true, mankind would not have been around to "clearly perceive" or see the world until billions of years **after** "the creation of the world." So, either theistic evolution is false, or Paul was in error and was not inspired by God—a contention which would eliminate much of the New Testament.

And further, Jesus, Himself, said in Mark 10:6 concerning Adam and Eve, "But from the beginning of the creation, God 'made them male and female'" (cf. Matthew 19:4; Genesis 1:27). Again, if theistic evolution were true, man was certainly not around "from the beginning of creation." Evolutionary theory supposes that mankind was not around for the vast majority of the Universe's history. If theistic evolution is true, Jesus, Himself—the Son of Almighty God—is in error and not worthy of our worship. Indeed, theistic evolutionary positions strike at the very heart of the Christian faith—the integrity and inspiration of the Bible, the inspiration of Moses and Paul, and the deity of Christ Himself.

Bottom line: theistic evolution cannot be harmonized with the scientific evidence, since evolution does not even have a mechanism for creating new creatures. It also has no grounds for support in Scripture. Consider: if it does not harmonize with the scientific or the biblical evidence, why support it? Why not trust the biblical model of Creation, which is supported by the evidence and therefore, unlike the evolutionary model, does not require a blind leap of faith to accept it?

Seek and Defend

Several have said to Apologetics Press personnel over the years, "Does it matter? What's the big deal if someone believes in theistic evolution?" The above Gallup poll, and the implications of belief in this devastating doctrine with regard to the biblical text, make it

clear that this matter is no "little thing." It is critical that Christians prepare themselves for the defense of the truth on any topic (1 Peter 3:15)—that they "search" and come to a knowledge of the truth (Acts 17:11). After all, truth—not ignorance or self-deception—will set us free (John 8:32). We are commanded to "prove" or "test all things; hold fast what is good" or right (1 Thessalonians 5:21). Sticking one's head in the sand and ignoring the subject is not a scriptural approach to dealing with the subject. The proper interpretation of the first chapter of the Bible is no exception to this command. Genesis one provides the foundation for the rest of the Bible. It is a cornerstone of the Christian worldview. The Christian should be ready to cast "down arguments and every high thing that exalts itself against the knowledge of God, bringing every thought into captivity to the obedience of Christ" (2 Corinthians 10:5).

Review Questions

1) Why should the atheist be interested in discussing evolution?
2) Discuss the effect that widespread naturalism would have on a society.
3) Discuss the results of the Gallup poll.
4) Why is theistic evolution a devastating doctrine?

"Even if There is a God, How Do You Know He's the God of the Bible?"

If one comes to the conclusion that God exists, the next, natural question one might ask is, "How do we know **which** God?" It is outside the scope of this book to answer that question in full (see www.apologeticspress.org for materials on the subject). However, suffice it to say that an analysis of creation helps us to see certain characteristics about the Creator (what creationists call "general revelation," which is supported by Romans 1:20; Psalm 19; and Acts 14:17), similar to how we might learn something about an inventor by his invention, or about parents by their children. The Creator has certain characteristics that do not harmonize with the false gods that have been invented by men. However, the God described in the Bible harmonizes with the evidence from nature.

One of those characteristics we can learn about the Creator is that He is concerned about His creation. It would make sense for such a Creator to communicate with His creation, and there are a few books in existence on Earth which claim to be from the Creator. However, when examined to see if these books, indeed, have divine characteristics, one by one they are rejected. **Only one** proves itself to have attributes that are beyond the capability of humans—thus categorizing it as a supernatural book. That book is the Bible. [NOTE: See www.apologeticspress.org for more on the lack of inspiration of other religious books.] The Bible has held up to the scrutiny and attacks of its critics and proven itself to be flawless, though written by some 40 men with drastically different backgrounds over a period of almost

1600 years. [NOTE: See Butt, 2007 for an examination of some of this evidence.]

When a person realizes that the Bible is the Word of God and he reads it, he will understand that God has expectations for humans—behaviors He expects of us, which will bring us long-term happiness. Though He gives us the option of rejecting Him, He warns us of the tragic consequences of choosing that path, namely, eternal punishment. Again, it is our choice. We can choose eternal blessings if we desire—if we are willing to become unselfish beings who comply with His prescription for happiness.

If we can help you in your search for God's way in the Bible, please do not hesitate to contact us at Apologetics Press. [NOTE: See www.apologeticspress.org for a wealth of information on the subject of salvation and God's requirements for mankind.]

References

Akahane, Hisatada, Takeshi Furuno, Hiroshi Miyajima, Toshiyuki Yoshi-kawa, and Shigeru Yamamoto (2004), "Rapid Wood Silicification in Hot Spring Water: An Explanation of Silicification of Wood During the Earth's History," *Sedimentary Geology*, 169[3-4]:219-228, July 15.

"Alien Life in Meteorites: 'Remarkable Achievement' or 'Garbage'?" (2011), *Fox News*, March 7, http://www.foxnews.com/scitech/2011/03/07/alien-life-meteorites-skeptics-believers-weigh/.

American Heritage Dictionary of the English Language (2000), (Boston, MA: Houghton Mifflin), fourth edition.

"Andrey Nikolayevich Kolmogorov" (2013), *Encyclopaedia Britannica Online*, http://www.britannica.com/EBchecked/topic/321441/Andrey-Nikolayevich-Kolmogorov.

Aquinas, Thomas (1952), *Summa Theologica*, trans. Fathers of the English Dominican Province (Chicago, IL: University of Chicago).

Arago, Francois (1857), *Biographies of Distinguished Scientific Men* (Boston, MA: Ticknor & Fields), http://www.gutenberg.org/files/16775/16775-h/16775-h.htm.

Archie, John (2012), "Philosophy 103: Introduction to Logic—*Argumentum Ad Populum*," *Introduction to Logic*, Lander University, http://philosophy.lander.edu/logic/popular.html.

Aristotle (1984), *Physics*, in *The Complete Works of Aristotle*, ed. Jonathan Barnes (Princeton, NJ: Princeton University Press).

Aristotle (2009), *Metaphysics*, trans. W.D. Ross, http://classics.mit.edu/Aristotle/metaphysics.1.i.html.

Arndt, William, F.W. Gingrich, and Frederick W. Danker (1979), *A Greek-English Lexicon of the New Testament and Other Early Christian Literature* (Chicago, IL: University of Chicago Press), second edition revised.

Asimov, Isaac (1970), "In the Game of Energy and Thermodynamics You Can't Even Break Even," *Smithsonian Institute Journal*, pp. 4-10, June.

"Astronomers Discover Complex Organic Matter Exists Throughout the Universe" (2011), *ScienceDaily*, The University of Hong Kong, October 26, http://www.sciencedaily.com/releases/2011/10/111026143721.htm.

Ayala, Francisco (1968), "Genotype, Environment, and Population Numbers," *Science*, 162:1436.

Ayala, Francisco (1978), "The Mechanisms of Evolution," *Scientific American*, 239[3]:56-59, September.

Balme, D.M. (1962), "Development of Biology in Aristotle and Theophrastus: Theory of Spontaneous Generation," *Phronesis: A Journal for Ancient Philosophy*, 7[1-2]:91-104.

Bataillon, T. (2000), "Estimation of Spontaneous Genome-wide Mutation Rate Parameters: Whither Beneficial Mutations?" *Heredity*, 84:497-501.

Baum, Robert (1975), *Logic* (New York: Holt, Rinehart, & Winston).

Behe, Michael (2007), *The Edge of Evolution* (New York: Free Press).

Behe, M.J. (2010), "Experimental Evolution, Loss-of-Function Mutations, and 'The First Rule of Adaptive Evolution,'" *The Quarterly Review of Biology*, 85[4]:419-445.

Benford, Gregory (2006), *What We Believe But Cannot Prove*, ed. John Brockman (New York: Harper Perennial).

Bergman, Jerry (2012), "Darwin Skeptics: A Select List of Science Academics, Scientists, and Scholars who are Skeptical of Darwinism," http://www.rae.org/darwinskeptics.html.

Berlinski, David (1998), "Was There a Big Bang?," *Commentary*, pp. 28-38, February.

Bernal, J.D. (1951), *The Physical Basis of Life* (London: Routledge & Kegan Paul).

Bernal, J.D. (1967), *The Origin of Life* (London: Weidenfeld & Nicolson), 3rd Impression.

Bernardes, A.T. (1996), "Mutation Load and the Extinction of Large Populations," *Physica ACTA*, 230:156-173.

"Biopoiesis" (2011), *Encyclopaedia Britannica Online*, http://www.britannica.com/EBchecked/topic/66167/biopoiesis.

"Bloodletting" (2012), Science Museum Brought to Life: Exploring the History of Medicine, http://www.sciencemuseum.org.uk/broughttolife/techniques/bloodletting.aspx.

Borel, Emile (1962), *Probabilities and Life* (New York: Dover).

Borel, Emile (1963), *Probability and Certainty* (New York: Walker).

Borel, Emile (1965), *Elements of the Theory of Probability* (Englewood Cliffs, NJ: Prentice-Hall).

Borgnakke, Claus and Richard E. Sonntag (2009), *Fundamentals of Thermodynamics* (Asia: John Wiley & Sons), seventh edition.

Burroughs, Laurence, Paul A. Clarke, Henrietta Forintos, James A. R. Gilks, Christopher J. Hayes, Matthew E. Vale, William Wade, and Myriam Zbytniewski (2012), "Asymmetric Organocatalytic Formation of Protected and Unprotected Tetroses Under Potentially Prebiotic Conditions," *Organic and Biomolecular Chemistry*, 10[8]:1565-1570.

Butt, Kyle (2006), "Does Death Imply Annihilation?" Apologetics Press, http://www.apologeticspress.org/APContent.aspx?category=11&article=1861.

Butt, Kyle (2007), *Behold! The Word of God* (Montgomery, AL: Apologetics Press), http://www.apologeticspress.org/pdfs/e-books_pdf/Behold%20the%20Word%20of%20God.pdf.

Butt, Kyle (2008a), "Are Diamonds 'Life's Best Friend'?," Apologetics Press, http://www.apologeticspress.org/APContent.aspx?category=12&article=1127.

Butt, Kyle (2008b), "The Bitter Fruits of Atheism (Part I)," *Reason & Revelation*, July, 28[7]:49-55, http://www.apologeticspress.org/pub_rar/28_7/0807.pdf.

Butt, Kyle (2010a), *A Christian's Guide to Refuting Modern Atheism* (Montgomery, AL: Apologetics Press).

Butt, Kyle (2010b), "New Findings Show Flaws in Old-Earth Dating Methods," http://www.apologeticspress.org/APContent.aspx?category=9&article=3770.

Butt, Kyle and Blair Scott (2011), *The Butt/Scott Debate: Does God Exist?* (Montgomery, AL: Apologetics Press), September 29.

Butt, Kyle and Dan Barker (2009), *The Butt/Barker Debate* (Montgomery, AL: Apologetics Press).

Carlson, Lisa (2008), "Cells and Seeds: Chapter 1," Botany 110 Lecture Outlines, Centralia College, http://www.centralia.edu/academics/bioscience/courses/bota110/outlines/ch1.html.

Cartwright, John (2000), *Evolution and Human Behavior* (London: Macmillan).

"Causality" (2009), *Collins English Dictionary—Complete & Unabridged*, 10th ed. (New York: HarperCollins Publishers), http://dictionary.reference.com/browse/Causality?x=35&y=25.

"Causality" (2008), *Concise Oxford English Dictionary* (Oxford, U.K.: Oxford University Press), 11th edition, http://www.diclib.com/causality/show/en/coed/C/6567/1260/12/22/16059.

Cavalli-Sforza, Luigi Luca (2000), *Genes, Peoples, and Languages* (New York: North Point Press).

"Cell Theory and Microscopes: An Introduction to Microscopy" (2013), Microscope Master, http://www.microscopemaster.com/cell-theory.html.

Cengel, Yunus A. and Michael A. Boles (2002), *Thermodynamics: An Engineering Approach* (New York: McGraw-Hill), fourth edition.

Cengel, Yunus A., Robert H. Turner, and John M. Cimbala (2008), *Thermal-Fluid Sciences* (New York: McGraw-Hill).

Central Intelligence Agency (2008), "The Day the Wall Came Down," June 20, https://www.cia.gov/library/center-for-the-study-of-intelligence/csi-publications/csi-studies/studies/vol52no2/iac/the-day-the-wall-came-down.html.

Central Intelligence Agency (2012), "CIA Celebrates Original Headquarters Building's 50th Anniversary," February 12, https://www.cia.gov/news-information/featured-story-archive/2012-featured-story-archive/cia-celebrates-original-headquarters-buildings-50th-anniversary.html.

Chain, Ernst (1970), *Social Responsibility and the Scientist in Modern Western Society* (London: Council of Christians and Jews).

Chaisson, Eric (2012), "Cosmic Evolution: From Big Bang to Humankind," Harvard College Observatory, https://www.cfa.harvard.edu/~ejchaisson/cosmic_evolution/docs/splash.html.

Chow, Denise (2011), "Discovery: Cosmic Dust Contains Organic Matter from Stars," *Space.com*, October 26, http://www.space.com/13401-cosmic-star-dust-complex-organic-compounds.html.

Chown, Marcus (2012), "In the Beginning," *New Scientist*, 216[2893]:33-35, December 1.

Clark, Stuart (2008), "Where Did Life Come From?" *New Scientist*, 199[2675]:30-31, September 27.

Clifford, John L. and John DiGiovanni (2010), "The Promise of Natural Products for Blocking Early Events in Skin Carcinogenesis," *Cancer Prevention Research*, 3:132, February, http://cancerpreventionresearch. aacrjournals.org/content/3/2/132.full.

Colley, Caleb (2010), "Aristotle's 'Unmoved Mover' and Those Who Are 'Without Excuse,'" Apologetics Press, http://www.apologeticspress.org/ APContent.aspx?category=12&article=3795.

Collins English Dictionary (2003), (New York, NY: HarperCollins Publishers), http://www.thefreedictionary.com/Logical+fallacy%2FEquivocation.

Conford, F.M. (1957), "Pattern of Ionian Cosmogony," in *Theories of the Universe*, ed. Milton K. Munitz (Glencoe, IL: Free Press).

Considine, Douglas M. (1976), *Van Nostrand's Scientific Encyclopedia* (New York: Van Nostrand Reinhold), fifth edition.

Coolidge-Stolz, Elizabeth, Jan Jenner, Marylin Lisowski, Donald Cronkite, and Linda Cronin Jones (2005), *Life Science* (Boston, MA: Prentice Hall).

Craig, William Lane (1994), "Creation and Big Bang Cosmology," *Philosophia Naturalis*, 31[1994]:217-224.

"Creation Scientists and Other Specialists of Interest" (2010), *Creation Ministries International*, http://creation.com/creation-scientists.

"The Creation Question: A Curiosity Conversation" (2011), *Discovery Channel*, August 7.

Crick, Francis (1981), *Life Itself: Its Origin and Nature* (New York: Simon & Schuster).

Crow, J.F. (1997), "The High Spontaneous Mutation Rate: Is it a Health Risk?" *Proceedings of the National Academy of Sciences, U.S.A.*, 94:8380-8386.

"Curiosity: Did God Create the Universe?" (2011), *Discovery Channel*, August 7.

Daniel, Lucy, Ed Ortleb, and Alton Biggs (1999), *Life Science* (New York: McGraw-Hill/Glencoe).

Darwin, Charles (1859), *On the Origin of Species By Means of Natural Selection, or the Preservation of Favoured Races in the Struggle for Life* (London: John Murray).

Davidheiser, Bolton (1969), *Evolution and Christian Faith* (Nutley, NJ: Presbyterian & Reformed).

Davies, Paul (1978), "Chance or Choice: Is the Universe an Accident?" *New Scientist*, 80[1129]:506-508, November.

Davies, Paul (2006), *New Scientist*, 192[2578]:35, November 18.

Davis, Percival and Dean Kenyon (1989), *Of Pandas and People* (Dallas, TX: Haughton).

Dawkins, Richard (1982), "The Necessity of Darwinism," *New Scientist*, 94:130-132, April 15.

Dawkins, Richard (1989), "Book Review" (of Donald Johanson and Maitland Edey's *Blueprint*), *The New York Times*, section 7, April 9.

Dawkins, Richard (2009), *The Greatest Show on Earth* (New York: Free Press).

"Definition: Rudolf Virchow" (2006), *Webster's Online Dictionary with Multilingual Thesaurus Translation*, http://www.websters-online-dictionary.org/definitions/Virchow.

De Vries, Hugo (1905), *Species and Varieties: Their Origin by Mutation*, ed. Daniel Trembly MacDougal (Chicago, IL: Open Court).

Deweese, Joe (2010), "Has Life Been Made From Scratch?" *Reason & Revelation*, 30[7]:49-51, July, http://www.apologeticspress.org/pub_rar/30_7/1007.pdf.

DeYoung, Don (2005), *Thousands...Not Billions* (Green Forest, AR: Master Books).

Dick, Steven J. (2005), "Why We Explore: Our Place in the Universe," NASA, http://www.nasa.gov/exploration/whyweexplore/Why_We_13.html.

Dickerson, Richard E. (1978), "Chemical Evolution and the Origin of Life," *Scientific American*, 239[3]:70-110, September.

Dose, K. (1983), "The Origin of Life," *Nachrichten aus Chemie, Technik und Laboratorium*, 31[12]:968-969.

Dose, Klaus (1988), "The Origin of Life: More Questions than Answers," *Interdisciplinary Science Reviews*, 13[4]:348.

Ducoff, Howard (2007), "University of Illinois Biophysics: The First Half-Century," Center for Biophysics and Computational Biology: University of Illinois at Urbana-Champaign, http://biophysics.illinois.edu/program/history.html.

"Edison's Patents" (2010), *The Thomas Edison Papers*, Rutgers University, http://edison.rutgers.edu/patents.htm.

Einstein, Albert (1905), "Does the Inertia of a Body Depend Upon Its Energy-Content?" *Annals of Physics*, 18:639-643, September.

Einstein, Albert (2007), *The World As I See It* (New York: BN Publishing), abridged edition.

Eiseley, Loren (1957), *The Immense Journey* (New York: Random House).

Elena, S.F., L. Ekunwe, N. Hajela, S.A. Oden, and R.E. Lenski (1998), "Distribution of Fitness Effects Caused by Random Insertion Mutations in Escherichia Coli," *Genetica*, 102-103[1-6]:349-358.

Ellis, George F.R. (2011), "Does the Multiverse Really Exist?" *Scientific American*, 305[2]:38-43, August.

Enoch, Nick (2012), "British Scientists Recreate the Molecules that Gave Birth to Life Itself," *Mail Online*, January 27, http://www.dailymail.co.uk/sciencetech/article-2092494/Life-sweet-New-clue-chemical-origins-sugar-molecules-DNA-recreated-scientists.html.

Erwin, Douglas (2000), "Macroevolution is More Than Repeated Rounds of Microevolution," *Evolution and Development*, 2[2]:78-84.

Estling, Ralph (1994), "The Scalp-Tinglin', Mind-Blowin', Eye-Poppin', Heart-Wrenchin', Stomach-Churnin', Foot-Stumpin', Great Big Doodley Science Show!!!" *Skeptical Inquirer*, 18[4]:428-430, Summer.

Estling, Ralph (1995), "Letter to the Editor," *Skeptical Inquirer*, 19[1]:69-70, January/February.

"Fallacies" (2012), The Writing Center at UNC Chapel Hill, http://writingcenter.unc.edu/handouts/fallacies/.

Ferguson, Kitty (1994), *The Fire in the Equations: Science, Religion, and the Search for God* (Grand Rapids, MI: Eerdmans).

Fishbane, Paul M., Stephen Gasiorowicz, and Stephen T. Thornton (1996), *Physics for Scientists and Engineers* (New Jersey: Prentice Hall), second edition.

Flew, Antony and Roy Varghese (2007), *There Is A God: How the World's Most Notorious Atheist Changed His Mind* (New York: HarperOne).

Flew, Antony G.N. and Thomas B. Warren (1977), *The Warren-Flew Debate on the Existence of God* (Jonesboro, AR: National Christian Press).

Gal, Joe (2011), "Louis Pasteur, Language, and Molecular Chirality. I. Background and Dissymmetry," *Chirality*, 23(1):1-16, January.

Gardner, Martin (2000), *Did Adam and Eve Have Navels?* (New York: W.W. Norton).

Gefter, Amanda (2010), "Touching the Multiverse," *New Scientist*, 205[2750]:28-31, March 6.

Gerrish, Philip J. and Richard E. Lenski (1998), "The Fate of Competing Beneficial Mutations in an Asexual Population," *Genetica*, 102/103:127-144.

Gibson, D.G., et al. (2010), "Creation of a Bacterial Cell Controlled by a Chemically Synthesized Genome," *Science*, May 20, http://www.sciencemag.org/cgi/content/abstract/science.1190719.

Gish, Duane T., Richard B. Bliss, and Wendell R. Bird (1981), *Summary of Scientific Evidence for Creation [Part I]*, Impact Article #95 (El Cajon, CA: Institute for Creation Research), http://www.icr.org/article/177/.

Gitt, Werner (2007), *In the Beginning was Information* (Green Forest, AR: Master Books), Kindle file.

Gould, Stephen Jay (1977), "The Return of Hopeful Monsters," *Natural History*, 86[5]:12-16, May.

Gould, Stephen J. (1980), "Is a New and General Theory of Evolution Emerging?" Hobart College speech, 2-14-80; quoted in Luther Sunderland (1984), *Darwin's Enigma* (San Diego, CA: Master Books).

Grassé, Pierre-Paul (1977), *The Evolution of Living Organisms* (New York: Academic Press).

Green, D.E. and R.F. Goldberger (1967), *Molecular Insights into the Living Process* (New York: Academic Press).

Greenstein, George (1988), *The Symbiotic Universe* (New York: William Morrow).

Gribbin, John (1981), "Of a Comet Born," *Science Digest*, 89[3]:14, April.

Grigg, Russell (1996), "Ernst Haeckel: Evangelist for Evolution and Apostle of Deceit," *Creation*, 18[2]:33-36, March.

Gubner, J.A. (2006), *Probability and Random Processes for Electrical and Computer Engineers* (Cambridge: Cambridge University Press).

Guth, Alan (1997), *The Inflationary Universe* (New York: Perseus Books).

Guth, Alan and Paul Steinhardt (1984), "The Inflationary Universe," *Scientific American*, 250:116-128, May.

Haeckel, Ernst (1876), *The History of Creation* (New York: D. Appleton).

Hartgerink, Jeffrey D., Elia Beniash, and Samuel I. Stupp (2001), "Self-Assembly and Mineralization of Peptide-Amphiphile Nanofibers," *Science*, 294:1684-1688, November 23.

Hatch, Robert (2002), "Sir Isaac Newton," *Professor Robert A. Hatch: The Scientific Revolution Homepage*, http://www.clas.ufl.edu/users/ufhatch/pages/01-courses/current-courses/08sr-newton.htm.

Hawking, Stephen (1988), *A Brief History of Time: From the Big Bang to Black Holes* (New York: Bantam).

Hawking, Stephen (2010), *The Grand Design* (New York: Bantam Books).

Hayward, Alan (1985), *Creation or Evolution: The Facts and the Fallacies* (London: Triangle Books).

Hazen, Robert (2005), *Origins of Life*, audio-taped lecture (Chantilly, VA: The Teaching Company).

Heeren, Fred (1995), *Show Me God* (Wheeling, IL: Searchlight Publications).

"Henry Ford" (2010), *Encyclopedia of World Biography*, http://www.notablebiographies.com/Fi-Gi/Ford-Henry.html.

"Henry Ford (1863-1947)" (2010), *About.com*, Inventors, http://inventors.about.com/od/fstartinventors/a/HenryFord.htm.

Hoffman, Jonathan (2005), "Scientific Theories More Than Guesses," http://www.alligator.org/app/pt2/051129column.php.

Hofstadter, Douglas R. (1980), *Godel, Escher, Bach: An Eternal Golden Braid* (New York: Vintage Books).

Holloway, Robert (2010), "Experts on Thermodynamics Refute Creationist Claims," http://www.ntanet.net/Thermo-Internet.htm.

Hoover, Richard B. (2011), "Fossils of Cyanobacteria in CI1 Carbonaceous Meteorites," *Journal of Cosmology*, 13, March.

Horgan, John (1991), "In the Beginning," *Scientific American*, 264:119, February.

Horgan, John (1996), *The End of Science* (Reading, MA: Addison-Wesley).

Horgan, John (2011), "Pssst! Don't Tell the Creationists, but Scientists Don't Have a Clue How Life Began," *Scientific American*, http://www.scientificamerican.com/blog/post.cfm?id=pssst-dont-tell-the-creationists-bu 2011-02-28.

Houts, Michael G. (2007), "Evolution is Religion—Not Science [Part I]," *Reason & Revelation*, 27[11]:81-87, November, http://www.apologeticspress.org/pub_rar/27_11/0711.pdf.

Houts, Michael G. (2011), "True Science is the Christian's Friend," Apologetics Press, http://www.apologeticspress.org/APContent.aspx?category=9&article=3572.

"How to Debate a Creationist" (2007), *Creationism versus Science*, Arguments, http://www.creationtheory.org/Arguments/DebatingTips.xhtml.

Hoyle, Fred (1981a), "The Big Bang in Astronomy," *New Scientist*, 92:521-527, November 19.

Hoyle, Fred (1981b), "Hoyle on Evolution," *Nature*, 294:105,148, November 12.

Hoyle, Fred and Chandra Wickramasinghe (1978), *Lifecloud* (New York: Harper & Row).

Hoyle, Fred and Chandra Wickramasinghe (1981), *Evolution from Space* (London: J.M. Dent & Sons).

Hoyle, Fred, and Chandra Wickramasinghe (1984), *Evolution from Space: A Theory of Cosmic Creationism* (New York: Simon & Schuster).

Hoyle, Fred and Chandra Wickramasinghe (1991), "Where Microbes Boldly Went," *New Scientist*, 91:415, August 13.

Hylton, Wil S. (2012), "Craig Venter's Bugs Might Save the World," *The New York Times*, May 30, http://www.nytimes.com/2012/06/03/magazine/craig-venters-bugs-might-save-the-world.html?pagewanted=all&_r=0.

"International Space Hall of Fame at the New Mexico Museum of Space History: Galileo Galilei" (2013), New Mexico Museum of Space History, http://www.nmspacemuseum.org/halloffame/detail.php?id=108.

Isaak, Mark (2005), "Claim CA118," The TalkOrigins Archive: Exploring the Creation/Evolution Controversy, http://www.talkorigins.org/indexcc/CA/CA118.html.

Isaak, Mark (2007), "Claim CE410," The TalkOrigins Archive: Exploring the Creation/Evolution Controversy, http://www.talkorigins.org/indexcc/CE/CE410.html.

Jackson, Wayne (1983), "Our Earth—Young or Old?" http://www.apologeticspress.org/rr/reprints/yng-old.pdf.

Jaroff, Leon (1996), "Life on Mars," *Time*, 148[9]:76-82, August 19.

Jastrow, Robert (1977), *Until the Sun Dies* (New York: W.W. Norton).

Jastrow, Robert (1978), *God and the Astronomers* (New York: W.W. Norton).

Jeffs, William (2006), "NASA Scientists Find Primordial Organic Matter in Meteorite," *NASA: Johnson Space Center*, Release J06-103, http://www.nasa.gov/centers/johnson/news/releases/2006/J06-103.html.

Jevons, W. Stanley (1888), *Elementary Lessons in Logic: Deductive & Inductive* (New York: MacMillan).

"Joseph Lister (1827-1912)" (2013), Brought to Life: Exploring the History of Medicine, *Science Museum*, http://www.sciencemuseum.org.uk/broughttolife/people/josephlister.aspx.

Kant, Immanuel (1787), *The Critique of Pure Reason* (South Australia: The University of Adelaide Library), second edition, trans. J.M.D. Meiklejohn, http://ebooks.adelaide.edu.au/k/kant/immanuel/k16p/.

Kant, Immanuel (2008), *Kant's Critiques: The Critique of Pure Reason, the Critique of Practical Reason, the Critique of Judgment* (Radford, VA: Wilder Publications).

Kelly, Fred C. (1989), *The Wright Brothers: A Biography* (New York: Harcourt, Brace, & Company).

Kempthorne, John (1977), "Praise the Lord," *Songs of the Church* (West Monroe, LA: Howard Publishing).

Kenny, Anthony (1980), *The Five Ways: St. Thomas Aquinas' Proofs of God's Existence* (South Bend, IN: University of Notre Dame Press).

Keosian, John (1964), *The Origin of Life* (New York: Reinhold).

Kerkut, George A. (1960), *The Implications of Evolution* (London: Pergamon).

King, A.L. (1962), *Thermophysics* (San Francisco, CA: W.H. Freeman).

Klotz, John (1985), *Studies in Creation* (St. Louis, MO: Concordia).

Kolb, Rocky (1998), "Planting Primordial Seeds," *Astronomy*, 26[2]:42-43.

Kuppers, Bernd-Olaf (1990), *Information and the Origin of Life* (Cambridge, MA: M.I.T. Press).

Kwok, Sun and Yong Zhang (2011), "Mixed Aromatic-Aliphatic Organic Nanoparticles as Carriers of Unidentified Infrared Emission Features," *Nature*, 479:80-83, November 3.

Lahav, Noam (1999), *Biogenesis: Theories of Life's Origins* (Oxford, England: Oxford University Press).

Lemonick, Michael D. (2011), "Alien Life Discovered in a Meteorite! Or Maybe Not," *Time Science*, http://www.time.com/time/health/article/0,8599,2057461,00.html.

Levine, J. (1983), "New Ideas About the Early Atmosphere," *NASA Special Report*, N. 225, Langley Research Center, August 11.

Lewontin, Richard (1997), "Billions and Billions of Demons," *The New York Review*, January 9.

"The Life of Thomas A. Edison" (1999), Library of Congress, http://mcmory.loc.gov/ammem/edhtml/edbio.html.

Linde, Andrei (1994), "The Self-Reproducing Inflationary Universe," *Scientific American*, 271[5]:48, November.

Lipson, H.S. (1980), "A Physicist Looks at Evolution," *Physics Bulletin*, 31:138, May.

Lucas, George, dir. (1999), "Star Wars Episode I—The Phantom Menace," Lucasfilm.

Lyons, Eric (2004), "Controversial Jericho," Apologetics Press, http://www.apologeticspress.org/apcontent.aspx?category=6&article=666.

Lyons, Eric (2007), "What Caused God?" Apologetics Press, http://www.apologeticspress.org/APContent.aspx?category=12&article=2216&topic=93.

Lyons, Eric (2011), "The Moral Argument for the Existence of God," *Reason & Revelation*, September, 31[9]:86-95, http://www.apologeticspress.org/pub_rar/31_9/1109.pdf.

Lyons, Eric and Kyle Butt (2008), *The Dinosaur Delusion: Dismantling Evolution's Most Cherished Icon* (Montgomery, AL: Apologetics Press).

Maddox, John (1994), "The Genesis Code by Numbers," *Nature*, 367:111, January 13.

"Major Religions of the World Ranked by Number of Adherents" (2007), http://www.adherents.com/Religions_By_Adherents.html.

Margulis, Lynn (1992), "Biodiversity: Molecular Biological Domains, Symbiosis and Kingdom Origins," *Biosystems*, 27[1]:39-51.

Margulis, Lynn and Dorion Sagan (2002), *Acquiring Genomes: A Theory of the Origins of Species* (New York: Basic Books).

Martin, C.P. (1953), "A Non-Geneticist Looks at Evolution," *American Scientist*, Vol. 41.

Mayr, Ernst (2001), *What Evolution Is* (New York: Basic Books).

McFadden, John J. (2000), *Quantum Evolution: The New Science of Life* (New York: W.W. Norton).

McGraw-Hill Dictionary of Scientific and Technical Terms (2003), pub. M.D. Licker (New York: McGraw-Hill), sixth edition.

McKivor, Fran (2010), "Thomas A. Edison Patent Award," *ASME: Setting the Standard*, http://www.webcitation.org/5umTifXDW.

McLean v. Arkansas Board of Education (1982), 529 F.Supp. 1255, 1264 (E.D. Ark.).

"Meteor Crater: The Most Well Known, Best Preserved Meteorite Crater on Earth!" (2013), Meteor Crater, http://www.meteorcrater.com/, January.

Meyer, Stephen C. (2004), "Intelligent Design: The Origin of Biological Information and the Higher Taxonomic Categories," *Proceedings of the Biological Society of Washington*, 117[2]213-239, http://www.discovery.org/a/2177.

Meyer, Stephen C. (2009), *Signature in the Cell* (New York: Harper Collins), Kindle file.

Miller, Dave (2003), "Blind Faith," Apologetics Press, http://www.apologeticspress.org/apcontent.aspx?category=11&article=444.

Miller, Dave (2008), *The Silencing of God* (Montgomery, AL: Apologetics Press).

Miller, Dave (2009), *Christ and the Continental Congress* (Montgomery, AL: Apologetics Press).

Miller, Dave (2011a), "Is Christianity Rational?" *Reason & Revelation*, June, 31[6]:50-59, http://www.apologeticspress.org/pub_rar/31_6/1106.pdf.

Miller, Dave (2011b), "Jesus Was Rational," Apologetics Press, http://www.apologeticspress.org/APContent.aspx?category=10&article=1245.

Miller, Jeff (2007), "God and the Laws of Thermodynamics: A Mechanical Engineer's Perspective," *Reason & Revelation*, 27[4]:25-31, April, http://www.apologeticspress.org/articles/3293.

Miller, Jeff (2008), "Off With Their Heads!" Apologetics Press, http://www.apologeticspress.org/APContent.aspx?category=7&article=2485.

Miller, Jeff (2011a), "A Review of *Discovery Channel*'s 'Curiosity: Did God Create the Universe?'" *Reason & Revelation*, 31[10]:98-107, October, http://www.apologeticspress.org/apPubPage.aspx?pub=1&issue=1004&article=1687.

Miller, Jeff (2011b), "Expelled—Again," Apologetics Press, http://www.apologeticspress.org/APContent.aspx?category=12&article=3655.

Miller, Jeff (2012a), "Another Pointless Attempt to Defeat Biogenesis," *Reason & Revelation*, 32[8]:77-80, August, http://www.apologeticspress.org/apPubPage.aspx?pub=1&issue=1090&article=2027.

Miller, Jeff (2012b), "Bill Nye: The (Pseudo-)Science Guy," Apologetics Press, http://www.apologeticspress.org/APContent.aspx?category=9&article=2842.

Miller, Jeff (2013), "Don't Assume Too Much: Not All Assumptions in Science Are Bad," *Reason & Revelation*, 33[6]:62-64,69-70, June, http://www.apologeticspress.org/apPubPage.aspx?pub=1&issue=1122&article=2153.

Miller, Kenneth R. and Joseph Levine (1991), *Biology* (Englewood Cliffs, NJ: Prentice Hall).

Miller, Kenneth R. and Joseph S. Levine (2006), *Biology* (Upper Saddle River, NJ: Prentice Hall).

Miller, Stanley L. (1953), "A Production of Amino Acids Under Possible Primitive Earth Conditions," *Science*, 117[3046]:528-529, May 15.

Mills, David (2006), *Atheist Universe: The Thinking Person's Answer to Christian Fundamentalism* (Berkeley, CA: Ulysses Press).

Moe, Martin (1981), "Genes on Ice," *Science Digest*, 89[11]:36, December.

Moore, John N. and H.S. Slusher (1974), *Biology: A Search for Order in Complexity* (Grand Rapids, MI: Zondervan).

Moran, Michael J. and Howard N. Shapiro (2000), *Fundamentals of Engineering Thermodynamics* (New York: John Wiley & Sons), fourth edition.

Morowitz, Harold J. (1970), *Entropy for Biologists* (New York: Academic Press).

Morris, H. (1974), "The Young Earth," *Acts & Facts*, 3[8], http://www.icr.org/article/young-earth.

Morris, Henry M. (1984), *The Biblical Basis for Modern Science* (Grand Rapids, MI: Baker).

Morris, Henry M. (1990), *Men of Science Men of God: Great Scientists Who Believed in the Bible* (El Cajon, CA: Master Books).

Morris, Richard (1990), *The Edges of Science* (New York: Prentice Hall).

Muller, Hermann J. (1950), "Radiation Damage to the Genetic Material," *American Scientist*, 38:33-50,126, January.

Nagy, Bartholomew, Warren G. Meinschein, and Douglas J. Hennessy (1963), "Aqueous, Low Temperature Environment of the Orgueil Meteorite Parent Body," *Annals of the New York Academy of Sciences*, 108:534-552, June.

Nakamura-Messenger, Keiko, Scott Messenger, Lindsay P. Keller, Simon J. Clemett, and Michael E. Zolensky (2006), "Organic Globules in the Tagish Lake Meteorite: Remnants of the Protosolar Disk," *Science*, 314[5804]:1439-1442.

National Geographic Education Division, Lucy Daniel, Peter Rillero, Alton Biggs, Edward Ortleb, and Dinah Zike (2005), *Life Sciences* (New York: McGraw-Hill/Glencoe).

Newport, Frank (2012), "In U.S., 46% Hold Creationist View of Human Origins," *GALLUP Politics*, June 1, http://www.gallup.com/poll/155003/Hold-Creationist-View-Human-Origins.aspx.

O'Connor, John J. and Edmund F. Robertson (2008), "Felix Edouard Justin Emile Borel," *The MacTutor History of Mathematics Archive*, http://www-history.mcs.st-andrews.ac.uk/Mathematicians/Borel.html.

Patterson, Colin (1981), *Speech given in November at American Museum of Natural History in New York City*. Quotations are from audio tape transcript. See Bethell (1985) for a report on Dr. Patterson's speech.

Pfeiffer, Charles F. (1972), *The Biblical World* (Grand Rapids, MI: Baker Book House).

Plato (1966), *Plato in Twelve Volumes*, trans. Harold North Fowler (Cambridge, MA: Harvard University Press), http://www.perseus.tufts.edu/hopper/text?doc=Perseus%3Atext%3A1999.01.0170%3Atext%3DPhaedo%3Asection%3D96a.

"Professor's Alien Life 'Seed' Theory Claimed" (2010), *BBC News*, February 1, http://news.bbc.co.uk/2/hi/uk_news/wales/south_east/8491398.stm.

Quastler, Henry (1964), *The Emergence of Biological Organization* (New Haven, CT: Yale University Press).

Quick, Clarence R. (1961), "How Long Can a Seed Remain Alive?" *Yearbook of Agriculture* (Washington, D.C.: The United States Government Printing Office), The United States Department of Agriculture, http://www.fs.fed.us/psw/publications/documents/misc/yoa1961_quick001.pdf.

Rensberger, Boyce (1986), *How the World Works* (New York: William Morrow).

Reynolds, Kelly (2009), "Discovery of Germs," The University of Arizona Mel and Enid Zuckerman College of Public Health, http://learnaboutgerms.arizona.edu/discovery_of_germs.htm.

Rifkin, Jeremy (1980), *Entropy: A New World View* (New York: Viking).

Ruby, Lionel (1960), *Logic: An Introduction* (Chicago, IL: J.B. Lippincott).

"Rudolf Virchow" (1973), *Encyclopaedia Britannica* (London: William Benton Publisher), 23:35.

Sagan, Carl, ed. (1973), *Communications with Extra-Terrestrial Intelligence* (Boston, MA: MIT Press).

Sallon, Sarah, Elaine Solowey, Yuval Cohen, Raia Korchinsky, Markus Egli, Ivan Woodhatch, Orit Simchoni, and Mordechai Kislev (2008), "Germination, Genetics, and Growth of an Ancient Date Seed," *Science*, 320[5882]:1464.

Sanders, Laura (2010), "Genome from a Bottle," *Science News*, May 20, http://www.sciencenews.org/view/generic/id/59438/title/Genome_from_a_bottle.

Sanford, J.C. (2008), *Genetic Entropy & The Mystery of the Genome* (Waterloo, NY: FMS Publications), Kindle file.

Sarfati, J.D. (1998a), "Origin of Life: The Chirality Problem," *Technical Journal*, 12[3]263-266, December, http://creation.com/origin-of-life-the-chirality-problem.

Sarfati, Jonathan D. (1998b), "If God Created the Universe, Then Who Created God?" *Creation Ex Nihilo Technical Journal*, 12[1]:21.

Sartre, Jean-Paul (1989), "Existentialism is Humanism," in *Existentialism from Dostoyevsky to Sartre*, ed. Walter Kaufman, trans. Philip Mairet (Meridian Publishing Company), http://www.marxists.org/reference/archive/sartre/works/exist/sartre.htm.

Scott, Andrew (1985), "Update on Genesis," *New Scientist*, 106:30-33, May 2.

Scott, Eugenie (2004), *Evolution vs. Creationism: An Introduction* (Los Angeles, CA: University of California Press).

Seaton, George (1947), "Miracle on 34th Street," Twentieth Century Fox.

Senapati, M.R. (2006), *Advanced Engineering Chemistry* (New Delhi: Laxmi Publications), second edition.

Shakespeare, William (2011), *Hamlet*, The Literature Network, http://www.online-literature.com/shakespeare/hamlet/10/.

Shapiro, Robert (1986), *Origins—A Skeptic's Guide to the Creation of Life on Earth* (New York: Summit).

Shermer, Michael (2006), *Why Darwin Matters* (New York: Henry Holt), Kindle file.

Shubin, Neil (2009), *Your Inner Fish* (New York: Vintage Books).

Shukman, David (2010), "Professor Stephen Hawking Says No God Created Universe," *BBC News*, September 2, http://www.bbc.co.uk/news/uk-11172158.

Simmons, K. (2007), "Cell Theory," *Cells and Cellular Processes Course Notes* (Winnipeg, Manitoba, Canada: University of Winnipeg), Fall, http://kentsimmons.uwinnipeg.ca/cm1504/celltheory.htm.

Simpson, George G., C.S. Pittendrigh, and L.H. Tiffany (1957), *Life: An Introduction to Biology* (New York: Harcourt, Brace).

Simpson, George G. and William S. Beck (1965), *Life: An Introduction to Biology* (New York: Harcourt, Brace & World).

Smith, Anthony (1975), *The Human Pedigree* (Philadelphia, PA: J.B. Lippencott).

Snyder, Leon A., David Freifelder, and Daniel L. Hartl (1985), *General Genetics* (Boston, MA: Jones and Bartlett).

Sommer, Andrei P., Dan Zhu, and Hans-Joerg Fecht (2008), "Genesis on Diamonds," *Crystal Growth & Design*, 8[8]:2628-2629, DOI: 10.1021/cg8005037.

Spencer, Herbert (1882), *First Principles: A System of Synthetic Philosophy* (New York: D. Appleton & Company), fourth edition.

Spielberg, Steven, dir. (1989), "Indiana Jones and the Last Crusade," Paramount Pictures.

Sproul, R.C., John Gerstner, and Arthur Lindsley (1984), *Classical Apologetics* (Grand Rapids, MI: Zondervan).

Stace, W.T. (1934), *A Critical History of Greek Philosophy* (London: Macmillan).

Stein, Ben and Kevin Miller (2008), *Expelled: No Intelligence Allowed* (Premise Media).

Stenger, Victor J. (1987), "Was the Universe Created?" *Free Inquiry*, 7[3]:26-30, Summer.

Stenger, Victor J. (2007), *God: The Failed Hypothesis* (Amherst, NY: Prometheus Books).

"Stephen Hawking Warns Over Making Contact with Aliens" (2010), *BBC News*, April 25, http://news.bbc.co.uk/go/pr/fr/-/2/hi/uk_news/8642558.stm.

Stober, David (2010), "The Strange Case of Solar Flares and Radioactive Elements," http://www.symmetrymagazine.org/breaking/2010/08/23/the-strange-case-of-solar-flares-and-radioactive-elements/.

Sullivan, J.W.N. (1933), *Limitations of Science* (New York: Viking Press).

Summers, Lawrence (2002), "Commencement Address," Harvard University, June 6, http://www.nps.gov/thje/memorial/inscript.htm.

Suplee, Curt (2000), *Milestones of Science* (Washington, D.C.: National Geographic Society).

"Synthetic Biology" (2012), OpenWetWare, http://syntheticbiology.org/.

Taylor, Chris (1997), "Is There Life on Mars?" *Time U.S.*, http://www.time.com/time/nation/article/0,8599,9976,00.html.

Taylor, Richard (1967), "Causation," in *The Encyclopedia of Philosophy*, ed. Paul Edwards (New York: Philosophical Library).

Teaching about Evolution and the Nature of Science (1998), National Academy of Sciences (Washington, DC: National Academy Press).

Thompson, Bert (1981), *The History of Evolutionary Thought* (Montgomery, AL: Apologetics Press).

Thompson, Bert (2000), *Creation Compromises* (Montgomery, AL: Apologetics Press), http://www.apologeticspress.org/pdfs/e-books_pdf/cre_comp.pdf.

Thompson, Bert (2001), "The Young Earth," http://www.apologeticspress.org/articles/1991.

Thompson, Bert (2004), "Is There Intelligent Life in Outer Space?" Apologetics Press, http://www.apologeticspress.org/APContent.aspx?category=9&article=1129.

Thompson, Bert and Brad Harrub (2003), "Have Scientists Created Life?: Examining the Miller-Urey Experiment," Apologetics Press, http://www.apologeticspress.org/APContent.aspx?category=9&article=1108.

Thompson, Bert, Brad Harrub, and Branyon May (2003), "The Big Bang Theory—A Scientific Critique [Part 1]," *Reason & Revelation*, 23[5]:32-34,36-47.

Thompson, Bert, Brad Harrub, and Eric Lyons (2002), "Human Evolution and the 'Record of the Rocks,'" Apologetics Press, http://www.apologeticspress.org/APContent.aspx?category=9&article=153.

Thompson, Silvanus P. (1910), *The Life of William Thomson Baron Kelvin of Largs* (London: MacMillan).

Thomson, William (1882), *Mathematical and Physical Papers* (Cambridge University Press).

Tryon, Edward P. (1973), "Is the Universe a Vacuum Fluctuation?" *Nature*, 246:396-397, December 14.

Tryon, Edward P. (1984), "What Made the World?" *New Scientist*, 101:14-16, March 8.

"Tsunamis" (2000), *The Oxford Companion to the Earth*, ed. Paul L. Hancock & Brian J. Skinner (Oxford University Press).

"Uniformitarianism" (2003), *McGraw-Hill Dictionary of Scientific and Technical Terms* (2003), pub. M.D. Licker (New York: McGraw-Hill), sixth edition.

"Uniformitarianism" (2012), *Merriam-Webster On-line Dictionary*, http://www.merriam-webster.com/dictionary/uniformitarianism.

United States Patent and Trademark Office (2008), "706.03(a) Rejections Under 35 U.S.C. 101[R 5]-700 Examination of Applications,",*Manual of Patent Examining Procedure*, http://www.uspto.gov/web/offices/pac/mpep/documents/0700_706_03_a.htm.

Van Wylen, Gordon J., Richard Sonntag, and Claus Borgnakke (1994), *Fundamentals of Classical Thermodynamics* (New York: John Wiley & Sons), fourth edition.

Vilenkin, Alex (2006), *Many Worlds in One: The Search for Other Universes* (New York: Hill & Wang).

Vilenkin, Alexander (1982), "Creation of Universes from Nothing," *Physics Letters*, 117B[1-2]:25-28, November 4.

Virchow, Rudolf (1858), "On the Mechanistic Interpretation of Life," in *Disease, Life, and Man: Selected Essays*, ed. by L.J. Rather (1958) (Stanford, CA: Stanford University Press).

Wald, George (1954), "The Origin of Life," *Scientific American*, 191:45-53, August.

Wald, George (1962), "Theories on the Origin of Life" in *Frontiers of Modern Biology* (Boston, MA: Houghton-Mifflin).

Walters, Tracy (1986), "A Reply to John Patterson's Arguments," *Origins Research*, 9[2]:8-9, Fall/Winter.

Warren, Thomas B. (1982), *Logic and the Bible* (Ramer, TN: National Christian Press).

Wells, Jonathan (2011), *The Myth of Junk DNA* (Seattle, WA: Discovery Institute Press).

Wiener, Norbert (1965), *Cybernetics: Or Control and Communication in the Animal and the Machine* (Cambridge, MA: M.I.T. Press).

Winchester, A.M. (1951), *Genetics* (Boston, MA: Houghton-Mifflin).

Wong, Gerard C.L., Jay Tang, Alison Lin, Youli Li, Paul Janmey, and Cyrus Safinya (2000), "Hierarchical Self-Assembly of F-Actin and Cationic Lipid Complexes: Stacked, Three-Layer Tubule Networks," *Science*, 288:2035-2039, June 16.

Yam, Philip (1997), "Exploiting Zero-Point Energy," *Scientific American*, 277[6]82-85.

Young, Willard (1985), *Fallacies of Creationism* (Calgary, Alberta, Canada: Detselig Enterprises).

Subject Index

[NOTE: See the Table of Contents for those topics that are discussed in depth throughout the book.]

Author Index

V

W

Y

Z